Y0-CDM-687

Barbara Klotz

Barbara Klotz

KIGER & CO., INC.
1830 W. 16th.
INDIANAPOLIS 7, INDIANA

POEMS
Children Enjoy

EDITED BY
Elizabeth F. Noon

ILLUSTRATED BY
Ruth B. Karb and James E. Palmer

F. A. OWEN PUBLISHING COMPANY
DANSVILLE, NEW YORK

To Elementary Teachers Everywhere

Who Have Helped Countless Girls and Boys
Enjoy Poetry

Acknowledgments

The editor and publisher make the following acknowledgments for reprint permissions: W. COLLINS AND COMPANY, LTD. for "Bobby Blue" by John Drinkwater from MORE ABOUT ME by John Drinkwater;   DOUBLEDAY & COMPANY, INC. for "The Dentist" by Rose Fyleman from THE FAIRY GREEN by Rose Fyleman, copyright, 1923, by Doubleday & Company, Inc.; "Mr. Minnitt" by Rose Fyleman from FAIRIES AND FRIENDS by Rose Fyleman, copyright 1926, by Doubleday & Company, Inc.; "Ice-cream Man" by Rachel Field from TAXIS AND TOAD-STOOLS by Rachel Field, copyright, 1926, by Doubleday & Company, Inc.; "Uncle Frank" by Monica Shannon from GOOSE GRASS RHYMES by Monica Shannon, copyright, 1930, by Doubleday & Company, Inc.;   MRS. ARTHUR GUITERMAN for "Chums" by Arthur Guiterman from THE LAUGHING MUSE (Harper);   HENRY HOLT AND COMPANY for "The Barber's" and "Tired Tim" by Walter de la Mare, and used by permission of the publishers;   J. E. H. WARTNABY, Executor of E. V. Lucas, for "Mr. Coggs, Watchmaker" by E. V. Lucas from PLAYTIME AND COMPANY by E. V. Lucas;   J. B. LIPPINCOTT COMPANY for "Circus" by Eleanor Farjeon from JOAN'S DOOR by Eleanor Farjeon, copyright, 1926, by Eleanor Farjeon, published by J. B. Lippincott Co.;   HOUGHTON MIFFLIN COMPANY for "The Dorchester Giant" by Oliver Wendell Holmes and "A Nautical Ballad" by Charles E. Carryl from DAVY AND THE GOBLIN by Charles E. Carryl;   THE MACMILLAN COMPANY for "Aunt Jane" from Herbert Asquith's PILLICOCK HILL, copyright, 1930, by Oxford University Press and used with the permission of The Macmillan Company; "At the Seaside," "The Cow," "Farewell to the Farm," "The Gardener," "The Lamplighter," "The Land of Story Books," "The Moon," "My Ship and I," "Rain," "The Sun's Travels," "Time to Rise," "The Wind," "Windy Nights," and "Wintertime" by Robert Louis Stevenson from A CHILD'S GARDEN OF VERSES.

Copyright © 1953, 1962, 1966, F. A. Owen Publishing Company, Dansville, New York

All rights reserved — Printed in the United States of America

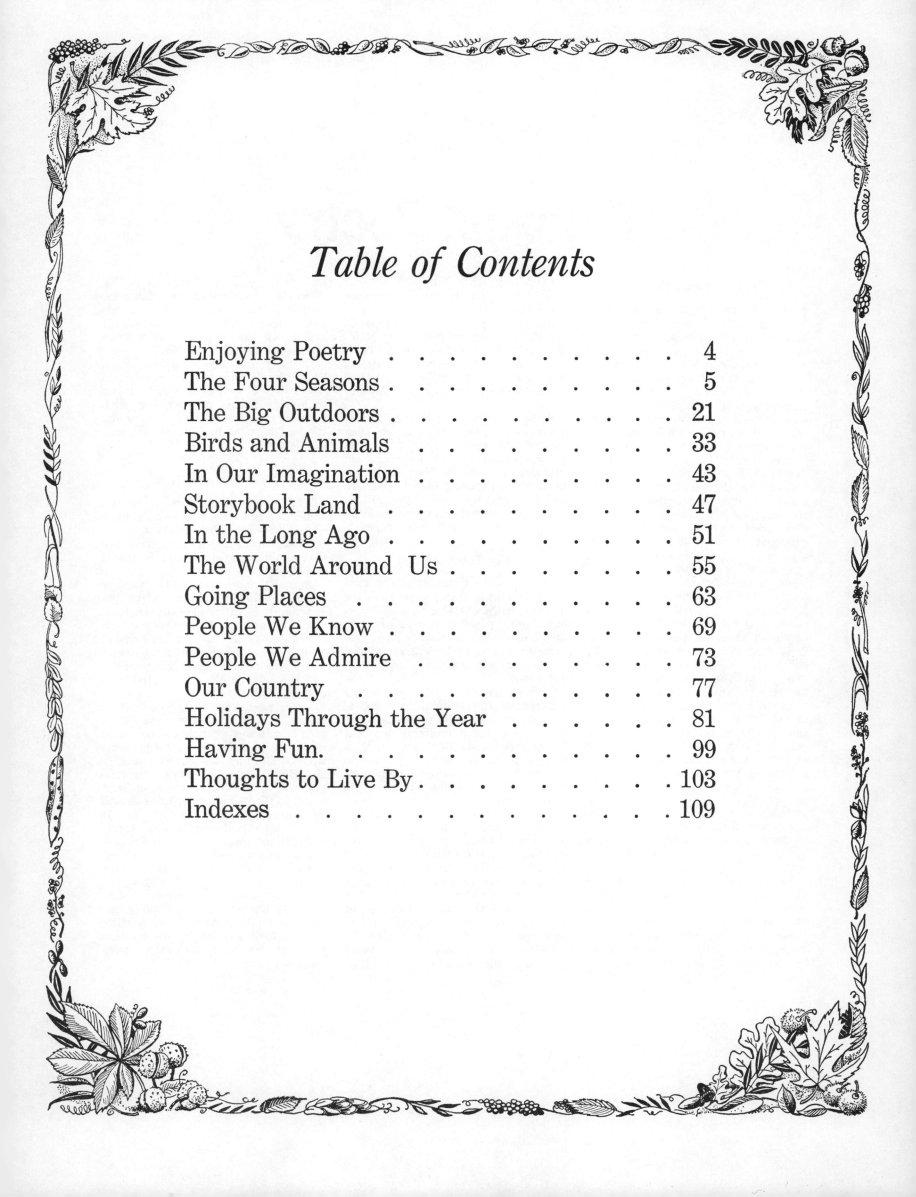

Table of Contents

Enjoying Poetry

How to Teach Poetry

LIKE an actor or actress who performs with an air of confidence and portrays the role in a seemingly effortless manner, so should one presenting poetry be well prepared.

A thorough reading, out loud if possible, will indicate how well you comprehend the rhythm, measure, and meaning. An accent accidentally may ruin the whole effect. Be prepared to make the poem live!

It is good to arrive at a general understanding of the poem before narrowing the discussion to the finer points of its construction. For instance, does it tell a story, give advice, tickle the funny bone, or merely comment on something in the world around us in a poetic manner? Once the intent of the writer is understood, it is easier to appreciate how he achieved his purpose.

Children may enjoy poetry more when it is read to them than when they read it themselves—at least when it is first introduced to them. The short irregular lines and phrases often seem confusing when compared to the simple and carefully planned prose they first read. Also, if caution is not taken in teaching a child to read poetry, he is likely to find it difficult and trying. This dislike is apt to carry over after he becomes adept at reading prose.

Choral reading is an outgrowth of an activity children enjoy—reading or talking aloud in unison. The whole group may want to say an especially rhythmic poem together or a few may say the poem while others move to or act out the rhythm.

Frequently children need help in pinning down their imagery, so that they hear the zooming airplane, or see the whirling leaf or creeping shadow, for they are often attracted more by the rhythm or rhyme than by the meaning. Reading aloud and then asking what they see or hear will help them learn to verbalize their reactions.

Nursery rhymes should not be ignored, for they are often the child's first introduction to poetry. Their rapid, lilting movements are attractive as well as a familiar beginning. Many children own a copy of Mother Goose.

Once children have learned to like poetry and enjoy reading it, they want to experiment in writing some. Encourage them to write about a pet cat, dog, a baby brother or sister. Remember, rhyming is not essential and insisting upon it may result in forced and stilted lines with much of the pleasure of writing destroyed.

Why Teach Poetry?

IF YOU asked a group of adults what poetry meant to them, some would be heartily enthusiastic, and a few perhaps would possibly remember poets they had studied with interest or perhaps marked distaste. The remainder would very likely show complete indifference.

This variety might be explained by differences in personalities, yet if you questioned the poetry lovers' group, you would probably see that these enthusiasts developed a very early appreciation of poetry. Parents and teachers who enjoyed poetry unconsciously passed their pleasure on to the children.

Some naturally have a greater sense of rhythm than others but practically every young child loves to run and dance or chant rhymes at play. The feeling for rhythm is developed early in life, and what is poetry but sound patterns. From the first "pat-a-cake" and clapping of hands a child experiences the enjoyable sensation of regular motion.

Children are imaginative without question. This is a quality to capitalize upon, for appreciation of poetry demands imagination and imagery. Ofttimes they will clap their hands with squeals of delight because of a pleasing mental picture in a poem that is being read.

Children are also natural mimics. They like nothing better than to be a "duck" or a "galloping pony." Many children's poems are written with mimicry in mind—galloping hoofs, the puff of a locomotive, or the swirl of the wind.

Make Poetry a Treat

POETRY is not a must. A person could live his whole life and experience it only superficially but certainly he would have missed an experience that could have given him hours of satisfaction.

Actually, satisfaction is the key word in using and appreciating poetry for it is fundamentally an emotional experience. If accuracy or deliberateness is the writer's goal, prose is his medium. But if he wants to lift the reader from the ordinary and the commonplace, he is likely to turn to poetry.

Every poem that was ever written is really a gift to the readers. It didn't have to be written—the world would have gone on just the same without it but the writer had a thought to express. When you present poetry to your children, make it a gift to them. The experience should be one they look forward to. It should give rest, inspiration, exhilaration, or genuine fun. Above all, it should never be tedious or required in the sense that the child is left with a burden that he doesn't enjoy.

The secret is to keep your eyes fastened to the end goal—lifelong enjoyment on the part of the participant. And if you lay the foundation for that, you will more than have achieved your goal.

The Four Seasons

VACATION

Vacation's full of jolly things
Like butterflies with yellow wings
And flowers that nod with every
    breeze,
While squirrels bark from tall oak
    trees;

But I am sure you cannot guess
What gives me greatest happiness.
It's this: I like the grass so sweet
That cools and tickles my bare feet.

EDDIE W. WILSON

THIS IS THE FALL

Grapes in the vineyard,
    Purple and dark;
Brown leaves are floating
    Down in the park.

Red are the apples,
    Plenty for all.
This is the harvest,
    This is the fall.

God gives us beauty;
    God gives us food.
God gives us all things
    Peaceful and good!

NONA KEEN DUFFY

A WINTER SURPRISE

Last night while I was sleeping
    The snow came softly down
And slipped on all the shrubbery
    A shining snowflake gown.

I guess that every little bush
    Felt startled with surprise
To find itself a cotton plant
    On opening up its eyes.

SOLVEIG PAULSON RUSSELL

SPRING

Skies are such a lovely blue;
    Grass is getting green;
Meadow is a cloth of gold,
    Waiting for the Queen.

Fields are bright with daffodils,
    Bluebirds on the wing;
Little brooklets run along,
    Keeping step with Spring.

WINIFRED C. MARSHALL

MARCH

Oh, March is a blustering
　Ruddy-faced boy,
Who blows out his cheeks
　And whistles for joy,
Who stamps through mud puddles
　And wades through slush,
Who never plays gently
　But always must rush.

He's a stout, sturdy fellow,
　Brimful of fun,
Who chases old Winter
　And makes him run.
Oh, he's rough and he's tough,
　But he has a kind heart,
And he's always on hand
　To help the Spring start.

SOLVEIG PAULSON RUSSELL

FEBRUARY FUN

In February, when the bark
Of maple trees is wet and dark,
And warm sunshine melts nighttime's
　freeze,
We know it's time to tap the trees.

Oh, making maple syrup's fun!
All day and night the sweet drops
　run,
Now fast, now slow, from a little
　spile—
A spout of wood. And all the while
We children tend the blazing fire
And rake the coals to flame up higher
Below the boiling kettle. Then,
With long, strong ladles, boys and
　men
Keep stirring the sap so it won't burn.
(I like to do my ladle-turn.)

To test the syrup, we drop spots
In nests of snow. Then when the dots,
Or pools, are cool, we sample them—
Each bit a brown and tasty gem.
Yes, making maple syrup's fun
From tapping the trees till the job
　is done.

HARRIETTE W. PORTER

OLD MAN MARCH WIND

That Old Man March Wind blusters
　through the town,
Twisting the tree tops, blowing chim-
　neys down,
Rattling the windows, shaking the
　doors,
Rushing around corners with howls
　and roars.

That Old Man March Wind will chase
　you down the street,
And if you're not careful, he'll blow
　you off your feet.
He'll set your hat spinning and snatch
　at your cloak,
And scatter your belongings, and
　think it all a joke.

Says Old Man March Wind, "I'm
　cleaning house for spring—
Sweeping up the rubbish, dusting
　everything,
Fanning the air, polishing the sky—"
Says Old Man March Wind, "I'm
　blowing winter by!"

JULIA POWELL

THE SUGAR CALL

Now flickers call, and robins call,
　And bluebirds in the wood,
"Oh, hurry, hurry, hurry!
　Here's sugar that is good.
"Oh, hurry, hurry, hurry!
　Bring buckets, spouts, and spoon,
The maple sap is running free
　In March's sunny noons
"Hepaticas are peeping through
　The dead leaves in the wood.
"Oh, hurry, hurry, hurry!
　Sugaring time is good.
"Oh, hurry, hurry, hurry!
　The snow is melting fast.
The time to gather sugar
　Will soon be quickly past."

NORMAN C. SCHLICHTER

MERRY MARCH

Merry, mad March comes in with a
　bound,
Tossing our caps and our kites all
　around,
Whisking the cobwebs out of the sky,
Teasing wee birdies just learning to
　fly,
Giving each tree-child a vigorous
　shake,
Telling each bud it is time to awake,
Jerking leaf-coverlets off sleepy
　heads,
Routing young flowerets from earthy
　beds,
Then with a song that makes work
　only play,
Merry, mad March goes dancing
　away.

NANCY FRITZ MOON

MAPLE SUGAR TIME

If city boys but knew the joys
　Of maple-sugar time,
I'm sure that they would right away
　Aboard some swift train climb,
And not get off till 'way up north
　Where maples yield their sap,
When comes the spring, and ev'ry-
　thing
　Awaits the pail and tap!

It's quite a tramp to reach the camp
　Deep in the silent wood,
But, oh, what fun for ev'ryone
　Who's in the neighborhood!
All gather round with merry sound,
　And start the sap to boil;
They stir and skim 'mid shadows dim,
　While songs make light their toil.

Then when we throw upon the snow
　The syrup hot, I'll say
That's a rare dish which all might
　wish
　To sample ev'ry day!
You'll never know unless you go
　Where maple trees abound
What loads of joy for girl or boy
　In sugaring off are found!

CLARENCE M. LINDSAY

THE RETURN

A new note of joy from the orchard,
A glimpse of a vest reddish-brown
A little gray head cocked sideways—
Sir Robin has come back to town.

He seems to be glad that I notice,
As I watch for his lady's down,
And call out to others in gladness,
"Sir Robin has come back to town."

Though Winter is ruddy and jolly,
Miss Spring is the maid of renown—
And our hearts sing a glad song of
welcome
When the Robins have come back to
town.

M. LUCILLE FORD

KITE SONG

All the other seasons
    Added up together
Never can compare
    With kite-flying weather!

Like a bird skimming
    Across the blue sky,
My kite travels swiftly—
    Beautiful and high!

The cord often runs
    Stinging through my hand,
As my bird soars higher,
    Higher o'er the land!

But all too soon twilight
    Lowers on the town,
And I must haul my bird
    Down, down, down!

ELAINE V. EMANS

OPEN THE DOOR

"Open the door!"
It's March that's knocking there so
    gay.
"Open the door!"
I've heard his merry, boisterous
    knock before;
Just hear him shouting, "Hurry,
    come and play,
And bring your kite, for it's a
    windy day!
Open the door!"

EVANTHA CALDWELL

WHY AM I GLAD?

Why am I glad when March winds
    blow?
Can't you guess? Don't you know?
Why, March winds toss my kite so
    high
It seems like an eagle in the sky.

And March winds drive the white
    clouds so
They look like sheep or drifts of snow.
They turn the windmills and play
    such jokes
As blowing off hats from common
    folks.

Why am I glad when March winds
    blow?
For all of these reasons. Besides I
    know
That the winds of March are the
    wings of spring,
And soon we'll have flowers and birds
    that sing.

SOLVEIG PAULSON RUSSELL

A MARCH SURPRISE

The trees are still asleep today
    And do not seem to know
A storm came by last night and
    heaped
    Their branches full of snow.

See how they start up with surprise
    As one by one they wake.
"Why, gracious me!" they seem to
    say,
    And give themselves a shake.

RALPH MARCELLINO

MARCH

Carefree March is here at last,
And the wintertime is past;
Now the happy bluebirds sing
Little lyrics of the spring.

Wild flowers waken from their sleep,
And through soft green curtains peep.
When the March winds romp and
    play,
April's never far away.

WINIFRED C. MARSHALL

FOR RENT

All winter the bird folk have lived in
    the South,
    But now with spring sunshine and
    rain
They're looking for signposts that
    lead to the North,
    And soon we shall see them again.

Some pleasant birdhouses I've put up
    for rent—
    Bird tenants, I hope, come along,
For this is the sign I have put at each
    door:
    These cottages rent for a song.

LELAND B. JACOBS

MARCH WIND

We made a brand-new kite today,
And soon as we were through
We came out here to fly it,
And the wind just blew and blew.
And now the kite's a tiny speck;
We've used up all the string;
I'd like to go and get some more.
Anne's such a tiny thing
To hold the kite all by herself;
I wouldn't let her try,
For fear I might look back and see
Anne sailing through the sky.

ELEANOR DENNIS

SPRING IN ME

The sun is warm, the wind is soft,
  And in our apple tree,
A little bluebird sings a happy
  Springtime song to me.

On the lawn, where snow lay deep
  Not many weeks ago,
A hundred gay and sun yellow
  Dandelions grow.

The breeze blows little powdery
  clouds
  Across a sky of blue
I feel like singing little tunes
  For spring is in me, too.

MARIAN KENNEDY

SPRING SONG

The violets are blooming
On hillside and in lane,
The meadow larks are broadcasting
That spring has come again.

The merry little brooklets
All run along and sing
This happy little theme song,
"It's spring! It's spring! It's spring!"

WINIFRED C. MARSHALL

THE COMING OF SPRING

How do I know that spring is here?
Because the world is full of cheer.
The crocuses and daffodils
Peep out from all the window sills;

The grass is getting soft and green;
The garden makes a pretty scene—
Forsythia bushes all unfold
And show their blooms of fairy gold;

The tulips of my garden wall
Are getting beautiful and tall;
The birds are coming back to stay
And serenade us every day.

The world is full of joy and cheer!
That's how I know that spring is
  here!

CARMEN LAGOS SIGNES

BECAUSE IT'S SPRING

My father spades the garden,
  My mother rakes the yard;
My brother sails his newest kite,
  'Cause the South Wind blows so
    hard.

The snow is melting, melting,
  Where once it piled so high,
And yesterday, for dinner,
  We had fresh pieplant pie.

The blackbirds hop and find long
    worms,
  They like to flirt and "grackle,"
The fluffy chickens cheep and cheep,
  The hens all cluck and cackle.

The robin chirps and twists his head,
  He doesn't really sing;
And yesterday I saw the flash
  Of a red-bird's lovely wing.

The big, white clouds go tumbling,
  Up where it's blue and high;
The tree tops are laughing shrieking,
  As the wind goes sailing by.

I run and shout and scamper,
  I jump and laugh and sing;
I feel so wild and happy,
  Because, you know, it's spring.

ALICE CURTIS

SPRING COSTUME

Our wee apple tree
  Is the prettiest thing;
She dressed herself up
  In her nicest this spring.

She put on a gown
  Of shimmering green,
The laciest gown
  That I ever have seen.

And then in the night,
  With the greatest of care,
She put diamond dew
  On the flowers in her hair,

Those lovely pink blooms,
  With a perfume so sweet;
The rest of the orchard
  All knelt at her feet.

MARIAN STEARNS CURRY

IT'S SPRING

Good-by, snow! Good-by, ice!
Though of course you're very nice,
I am glad you've gone away
Leaving us this fine spring day.

Here's my good old bat and ball!
Marbles, too! How are you all?
I am sure that I can play
With you now, 'most any day.

Good-by, winter! Though it's true
I've had lots of fun with you,
Now I just could shout and sing;
I'm so glad because it's spring!

WINNIFRED J. MOTT

HAPPIEST TIME

Spring is such a happy time—
  So many things to do;
Fields are bright with buttercups
  And wild flowers, pink and blue.

Strawberries grow beyond the hill;
  The meadow larks all sing.
Oh, there's no season in the year
  So wonderful as spring.

WINIFRED C. MARSHALL

THE ANSWER

How do I know it's springtime?
  I hear a robin's song,
I see the springtime flow'rs in bloom
  The garden path along.

I've seen the syrup buckets
  Sway gently in the breeze,
I've found some pussy willows,
  And buds are on the trees.

But had I not the eyes to see,
  Nor ears, nor voice to sing,
My heart would tell me this glad
    news:
  "It's spring! It's spring!
    It's spring!"

LELAND B. JACOBS

POEMS CHILDREN ENJOY

WHO'D FORGET?

When March is going, going,
    To robins' gay farewell,
And April, blossom-laden,
    Is close to hill and dell;

When March is going, going,
    Oh, none would have her stay,
But who'd forget to thank her
    For preparing April's way?

NORMAN C. SCHLICHTER

RECIPE FOR SPRING

Mix returning robins gay
With some brave buds sprout-
    ing;
Add some pussy willows gray,
Starting on their outing.

Take a lot of melting snow,
Stream banks overflowing;
A few belated snowflakes
That don't know where
    they're going.

Add a V-shaped flock of
    geese
Against a cloudy sky,
And some jolly paper kites
That soar away up high.

Let a fussy gust of wind
Mix them well together,
And you'll have a mad March
    day
With hints of springtime
    weather.

ALICE CROWELL HOFFMAN

CHILD'S SONG IN SPRING

O Bluebird and Robin,
    O Catbird and Wren,
I want you to rent
    Our birdhouses again.

I'm lonely all winter
    When you've gone away.
Your song is as welcome
    As flowers in May.

S. MYRONE McGINLEY

SPRING IS COMING

March has warmed the icy blasts,
And the wintertime is past.

Now we hear the robins sing—
Happy harbingers of spring.

Little buds will wake from sleep,
From the ground their faces peep.

Do you know why all is gay?
Spring is not so far away.

DOROTHY HEVENER

MARCH

You're loud,
You're noisy,
    A blustery old chap!
You whistle,
You moan,
    You tear at my cap!

You blow,
You scowl,
    But, March, you are fair!
Part lion,
Part lamb,
    Now spring's in the air!

MILDRED PITTINGER

WELCOME TO SPRING

Gone are the snowdrifts, so icy and
    deep.
Welcome to spring, welcome to
    spring.
Flow'rets are waking from long win-
    ter's sleep;
Welcome to spring, to the spring.
Birds now return from their home in
    the south;
Nature is stirring, within and with-
    out,
And cold winter is soon put entirely
    to rout;
Welcome to spring, to the spring.

First, little crocus will peep through
    the ground,
Welcome to spring, welcome to
    spring.
Next, yellow jonquils will soon be
    around;
Welcome to spring, to the spring.
Down by the creek pussy willows
    awake,
Wild creatures too, from the naps
    that they take;
Birds fill the air with the songs that
    they make;
Welcome to spring, to the spring.

Soon will the bushes be covered with
    green,
Welcome to spring, welcome to
    spring.
Buds and then blossoms are every-
    where seen;
Welcome to spring, to the spring.
Out in the fields little lambs are at
    play;
Nearby are children, happy and gay;
Warm, mellow sunshine has now
    come to stay;
Welcome to spring, to the spring.

ELIZABETH HUTCHISON

THE FOUR SEASONS

INTERLUDE

A-clitter, a-clatter! I wonder what's
    the matter?
Why this splashing and this dashing
    against my window pane?

It's just the merry ditty, so musical
    and pretty,
The tapping, rapping spring song of
    the merry April rain.

A-pitter, a-patter! Now something is
    the matter.
What's the glimmer and the glitter
    on the still wet pane?

Oh, it's just a sunbeam smiling, so
    bewitching, so beguiling—
A brilliant interlude between the
    spring songs of the rain.

            M. LUCILLE FORD

THE FRIENDLY SHOWER

We like a friendly little shower
Which lasts quite often half an
    hour—
    The flowers and I—

It flies across the hillside fast,
And finds our pleasant garden last,
    Then hurries by.

We like a little friendly shower,
And never mind the dark clouds that
    lower—
    The flowers and I—

For soon the golden sun peeps out,
The fountain leaps with joyous shout,
    Blue smiles the sky.

            ALICE THORN FROST

APRIL SHOWERS

April skies are weeping
    Tears of silver rain
On the buds still sleeping
    In the verdant lane.

Now the clouds which lower
    Clear in dazzling light,
And the sudden shower
    Yields to sunbeams bright!

April's merely chaffing!
    First, the raindrops cool;
Then the bright skies laughing—
    Playing April Fool!

            CLARENCE M. LINDSAY

SPRING RAIN SONG

Cheerily the silver rain
    Knocks upon the windowpane.
Patter! Patter! Hear the sound!
On the roofs and on the ground.
Beating out a quick refrain,
    Hear the music of the rain.

Gentle spring has come at last;
    Winter now is overpast.
Drenched are forest, field, and glen;
Brought to life is earth again.
Beating out a gay refrain,
    Hear the music of the rain!

Little children love the rain,
    As it splashes on the pane;
Watch the streams that swiftly pour
Sidewalks and the roadside o'er.
Cry they, "Welcome, rain of spring,
    For the treasures that you bring."

            MAY B. BRYANT

APRIL RAIN DANCE

Pitter! Patter! drops of rain
Dancing on the windowpane!
Sometimes fast and sometimes slow
Up and down the glass they go,
Making their own music sweet
With the patter of their feet—
April!
    April!
        April!

Pitter! Patter! tinkling sound
As they madly whirl around;
Pit-ter! Pat-ter! sudden change
To a tempo low and strange.
See the rainbow jewels shine
On crystal slippers beating time—
April!
    April!
        April!

            MARION DOYLE

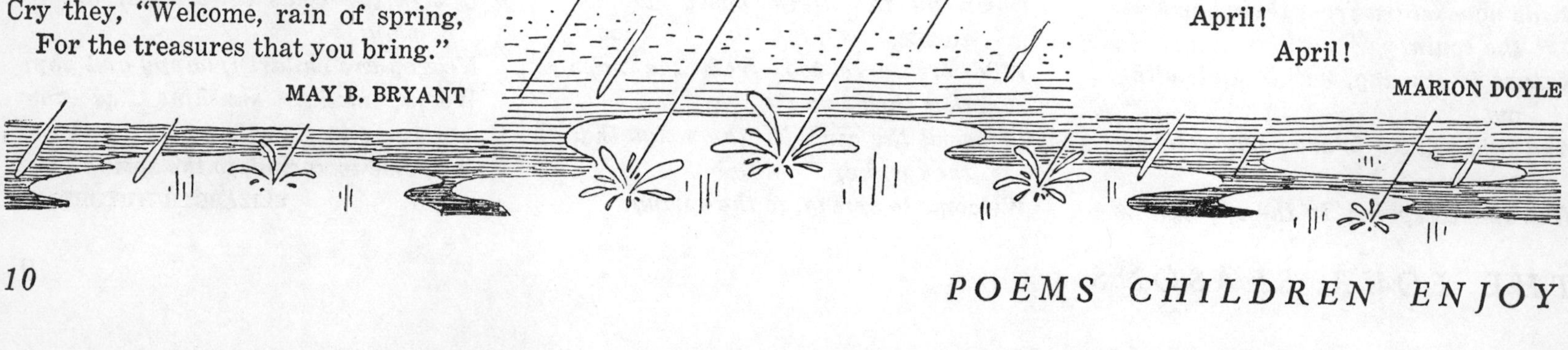

GUEST TIME

When we're expecting company
  Mother sets our house in shape;
No particle of dust and dirt
  Her brush and broom escape.

And Mother Nature does, you see,
  The very selfsame thing;
She makes March sweep her house
    quite clean
  For her gay guest, Miss Spring.

ALICE CROWELL HOFFMAN

APRIL FOOL

A snowfall came on April first,
  After the buds were out.
The pussy willows shook their heads.
  It made the crocus pout.

The bluebirds hopped from branch to
    branch,
  But never stopped their song;
They knew the snow was just a joke,
  And couldn't stay there long!

INEZ GEORGE GRIDLEY

SIGNS OF SPRING

Tops are whirling,
Kites are swirling
  In the windy sky;

Hoops are rolling,
Children strolling;
  Surely spring is nigh.

Brooks are flowing,
Grasses growing,
  Birds are nesting, too;

Buds are breaking,
Flowers awak'ning;
  Spring's come back to you!

MABEL NIEDERMEYER

A SPRING MORNING

It's easy to wake up in spring—
  Oh, yes, it's really so—
To dress, then very quickly
  Down to my breakfast go.

For why should I stay in bed?
  A foolish thing to do!
When all the flowers are wide awake,
  I have to wake up, too.

ALIX THORN

THE BLUEBIRD

"Dear little blossoms down under the snow,
You must be weary of winter, I know;
Hark, while I sing you a message of cheer;
Summer is coming and spring-time is here!

"Little white snowdrop! I pray you arise;
Bright yellow crocus! come, open your eyes;
Sweet little violets, hid from the cold,
Put on your mantles of purple and gold;
Daffodils! Daffodils! say, do you hear?—
Summer is coming and springtime is here!"

EMILY HUNTINGTON MILLER

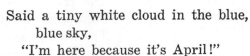

A Welcome Month Is April

Said a tiny white cloud in the blue,
    blue sky,
  "I'm here because it's April!"
And one golden ray of the sun replied,
  "I always shine in April!"
Then came a great storm cloud, with
    heavy gray sack,
And said, "Little sunbeam and cloud,
    you come back!"
He packed them away and I heard
    him say,
  "It always *rains* in April!"

Said a tiny green brook as it laughed
    along,
  "I'll sing to welcome April,"
And the bluebird returning soon
    heard the song
  And said, "I'll trill for April."
Then that rascal Jack Frost, with his
    merriest laugh,
Sent snowflakes a-flying all over the
    path!
Said the bird to the brook, "Will you
    please to look—
  There's *snow* again, in April!"

Said a wee little girl with golden hair
  "I need spring clothes in April!"
But the chill of the wind made her
    aunt declare,
  "It's always *cold* in April!"
Then, will you believe it, that very
    same day
The round sun invited the south wind
    to play—
The air was as warm as a day in May,
  Though it was only April!

I think you'll agree with me when I
    say,
  "A question mark is April."
The clouds and the sun and the South
    winds play
  Their merry tricks in April!
So, when it is sunny look out for a
    shower,
And though it is shining, 'twill rain in
    an hour—
Whatever the weather we say to-
    gether,
  "A welcome month is April!"

SARAH GRAMES CLARK

APRIL FLOWERS

Sing a song of April flowers,
Colors bright in all.
Crocus buds inside the gate,
Tulips by the wall,

Daffodils and lilies fair
In the garden green,
These with other April flowers
Make a pleasant scene.

Colors yellow, pink, and blue
Mingle with the red.
Rainbow colors everywhere
'Round the violet bed.

Sing a song of April flowers,
Colors bright and gay,
Making peaceful Easter scenes
For the holiday.

DOROTHY HEVENER

MAY

May always brings the sunshine,
    May baskets, Mother's Day;
We always crown a May queen
    Upon the first of May.

The wild flowers spread a carpet;
    The larks and thrushes sing,
Broadcasting from the tree tops
    Sweet lyrics of the spring.

Around the stately Maypole,
    We weave the ribbons gay;
There's something very lovely
    About the month of May.

WINIFRED C. MARSHALL

HERALD OF SPRING

Hark! the sounds of spring I hear,
Falling blithely upon my ear:
Twitter of birds in the maple trees,
Flutter of wings, and the humming of
    bees.

Fleecy clouds in a sky of blue,
Sparkling sunbeams sifting through,
Buds of flowers and greening grass
Nod to greet me as I pass.

Singing brooks reflect the sun,
Children through the meadows run,
As their greeting too they bring,
Welcoming the lovely spring.

WYROA HANSEN

THE COMING OF MAY

May opened up her basket,
And I looked in to see
    A sky of blue,
    The great sun too,
Both smiling out at me.

May opened up her basket,
And out the flowers fell.
    Their fragrance spilled
    Until it filled
All nature with its spell.

May opened up her basket,
Her choristers were there!
    Their welcoming
    To joy and spring
Was wafted on the air.

She opened up her basket—
The world was blithely gay.
    Earth knew again
    The ample reign
And blessing of the May!

LELAND B. JACOBS

A PARTY GUEST

I had a birthday party
    And a spring breeze came.
It hadn't been invited, but
    It joined us just the same.

It slipped in at the window
    Just in time to take
Part in blowing out
    The candles on my cake.

LUCRETIA PENNY

MAYTIME

Springtime came a-Maying
Over meadow, valley, hill,
In the early dawning
When all the earth was still.

Here she dropped a tulip,
There a lily fair,
And daffodils have fallen
From her flower-wreathed hair.

Over by the hedgerow
She dropped some violets down.
She left her posy tokens
At every door in town.

M. LUCILLE FORD

THE CALL OF SPRING

When spring begins
    Again to light
Our happy world
    With colors bright,

The robins all come
    Back to see
How beautiful
    The earth will be,

With crocus gold,
    And daffodils
Lighting meadows,
    Fields, and hills;

With leaves of green
    And tulips gay,
And birds arriving
    Every day.

NORMAN C. SCHLICHTER

MAY IS...

A blue sky shot with sunbeams,
Green shadows 'neath the trees,
The caroling of many birds,
A gentle, soft, warm breeze.

The fruit trees all in blossom,
Pale pink and pearly white,
The lilacs waving purple plumes,
A truly gorgeous sight.

Each flowering shrub a beautiful
Gigantic sweet bouquet,
In the month of birds and flowers,
Fragrant, lovely, merry May.

MAUDE M. GRANT

APRIL

Robin building, lark a-singing,
    Saucy jay has come;
Brooks a-murmuring, bees a-hum-
    ming,
Flowers peeping, wild things creep-
    ing,
    Winter's on the run;
Showers—then the sun;
Trees for planting, paths for hiking,
    Joy for everyone;
Roller skating, ropes for skipping,
    Mud pies almost done;
Marbles clicking, tops a-spinning—
    Isn't April fun!

MABEL HARMER

SUMMER'S INVITATION

Summer in a pleasant mood
At the school door smiling stood.
Smiling there she seemed to say,
"Come, it's time for rest and play;
Time for swimming and baseball;
Time to heed my cheery call
Off to hills and meadows free,
Off to woodland camp, or sea;
Time for hobbies specially planned
For vacation's wonderland;
Time for circus and parade;
Picnic time in park and glade."
In her pleasant restful way,
Summer beckons all today.

LELAND B. JACOBS

SCHOOL

When school lets out in June, I feel
As happy as can be.
I hop and skip and jump and run
And shout and laugh with glee.
I'm sure that I will never want
To go to school again,
But when September comes around,
I always like to then.

IVA RIEBEL JUDY

GOING FISHING

I've got my fishing tackle
And now that school is out,
I think I'll go a-fishing
To catch a mess of trout.
I borrowed a big shovel
From Jones's hired man.
I dug a lot of worms,
And put them in this can.
See this great big fellow!
Oh, boy, but he can squirm!
Any fish would bite, I guess,
At such a juicy worm.
I found this good old pole,
And then I bent this pin,
So now that I am ready
I might as well begin.

SOLVEIG PAULSON RUSSELL

ROLLER SKATING

Swing, glide, sway and roll,
Watch for the cracks and jump the hole,
Over the walks, under the trees,
Skating along as fast as I please.

Clump, clump! over the grass,
Stepping aside for the ladies to pass.
Swing, glide, roll and sway,
Skating is fun on a sunny day.

FRANCES ARNOLD GREENWOOD

CAMPING

Summertime has come again
And camping days are here,
With fishing, swimming, boating, too—
The best time of the year.

We climb the trees and go on hikes,
And all grow strong and brown.
Our friends will hardly know us
When we go back to town.

We do not miss the telephone,
The movies, or the cars,
When we can fish and hike all day,
And sleep beneath the stars.

WINIFRED C. MARSHALL

I'M SKIPPING

I'm skipping! I'm skipping! Heigh-ho
   and heigh-ho!
September's fine skipping time. See
   how I go!

I speed like the wind; like a bird flying high;
Like fast-darting stars in the top of
   the sky.

The world's filled with joy, and my
   heart's filled with song
When I'm skipping gaily, oh, gaily
   along!

I skip to my schoolroom as quick as a
   wink,
And home like an arrow, but what do
   you think?

My friends who don't skip say there's
   nothing much to it!
Their minds would be changed and
   hearts, too, if they'd do it.

      BERTHA REYNOLDS HUDELSON

SEPTEMBER

September is a lady
In a russet gown;
She marches through the country;
She marches through the town;
She stops at every schoolhouse
And rings a magic bell;

She dances on each doorstep
And weaves a magic spell.
She weaves a magic spell that goes
Winging through the land
And gathers children back to school
In a joyous band.

      SOLVEIG PAULSON RUSSELL

AUTUMN GOLD

King Midas went walking one beautiful day
In early October—or late in September—
A fine day for a walk, if I rightly
   remember!

The whole of the meadow he chose as
   his way
And all up and down both sides of the
   brook,
Gold daisies sprang up at each step
   that he took!

Next he entered the woods feeling, oh,
   very gay,
And every leaf in it this marvelous
   fellow
Touched into gold of most dazzling
   yellow!

Now, when you go strolling, as surely
   you may,
And find the world golden—there's no
   use in talking—
You know that King Midas himself
   has been walking!

      EVANTHA CALDWELL

AN AUTUMN PARTY

Autumn gave the leaves a party
   On a crisp, sunshiny day,
Clothed them all in gay new dresses,
   Sent them out to romp and play.

Dancing with the merry breezes,
   Happy hours passed all too soon,
Till they saw the evening shadows
   Chased away by Mr. Moon.

Then the sleepy little breezes
   Said, "We are too tired to roam";
And the frightened leaves cried sadly,
   "We can never get back home!"

But the old Earth Mother tucked them
   In a hollow, warm and deep,
Where they cuddled down together
   And went safely off to sleep.

      ANNA M. PRIESTLEY

SCHOOL

School bells are ringing, loud and
   clear;
Vacation's over, school is here.

We hunt our pencils and our books,
And say good-by to fields and brooks,

To carefree days of sunny hours,
To birds and butterflies and flowers.

But we are glad school has begun,
For work is always mixed with fun.

When autumn comes and the weather
   is cool,
Nothing can take the place of school.

      WINIFRED C. MARSHALL

The Color Carnival

Autumn comes dancing over the land,
Bringing a magic wand in his waving
   hand,
Calling a challenge to each frosty
   band.
Jack Frost starts gaily, leading the
   rest;
In a silver-white costume Jackie is
   dressed.
And what he is carrying maybe
   you've guessed!

It's a big pot of paint! And close on
   his heels,
The little frost fairies with frolicsome
   squeals
Come racing and laughing with musi-
   cal peals.
With small pointed brushes stuck in
   their caps
They dance on the ground with tip-
   pety-taps,
And each little coat-tail flippety-flaps!

When all of a sudden each little frost
   fay
Starts busily mixing the paint colors
   gay,
And hastens with brushes to work
   right away!
Painting the autumn leaves red, gold,
   and brown—
A gay color carnival over the town—
Each dear little frolicsome frost fairy
   clown!   CORA MAY PREBLE

GOLDEN DAYS

Everybody's busy,
The harvest days are here,
Time to gather golden grain,
For Winter's creeping near!

Farmers in the grainfields,
Bright with autumn sun,
Children in the woodlands,
Nutting time has come!

Squirrels a-chatter in the trees
Seem to sharply scold:
"Don't take every nut, we pray—
Winter's long and cold!"

FRANCES GORMAN RISSER

LEAF BLANKETS

Leaves are falling, soft as snowflakes,
    Red and yellow, gold and brown;
The breeze laughs gaily in the tree-
        tops,
    Shaking all the color down.

Leaves are covering the gardens
    As my blanket covers me.
When cold winter comes, the flowers
    Will be warm as warm can be.

IRENE B. CROFOOT

TUMBLE-DOWN DICK

Tumble-down Dick was a little red
        leaf,
    Who danced on the bough of a tree.
He skipped, and he hopped;
He tumbled and dropped;
    And his antics were wondrous to
        see.

He fell to the ground, but he couldn't
        lie still
    And wait to be raked in a heap.
He whisked and he whirled;
He twisted and twirled;
    And he ended each dance with a
        leap.

Though he knew that Old Winter
        should find him some night
    And tell him he must go to bed,
He hied and he hurried;
He scampered and scurried;
    Turned cart wheels and stood on
        his head.

INEZ WAHL

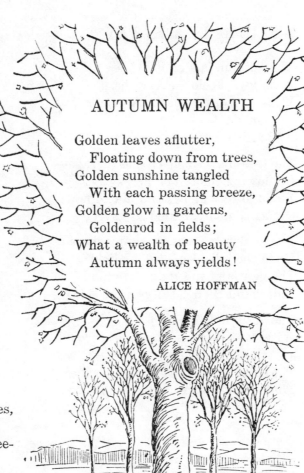

AUTUMN WEALTH

Golden leaves aflutter,
    Floating down from trees,
Golden sunshine tangled
    With each passing breeze,
Golden glow in gardens,
    Goldenrod in fields;
What a wealth of beauty
    Autumn always yields!

ALICE HOFFMAN

THE GIFTS OF AUTUMN

Autumn is hazy
    And brilliant and dry.
Its deep blue burns
    In the heavy sky.

Autumn is lavish
    With frosted nuts
And purple grapes
    Where the high field juts

Against the wood.
    Autumn tumbles down
A wealth of color
    On country and town,

A riot of leaves,
    A harvest of fruit,
And stalk and seed
    And berry and root.

And then when the sudden
    Twilight falls,
Autumn's best gift
    Is between four walls—

A blazing fire
    And a kitten near
And popcorn and apples
    And stories and cheer!

REVAH SUMMERSGILL

LEAVES OF AUTUMN

When blades of grass are turning
        brown
And autumn leaves come floating
        down,
I dance with them on lawn and street
And scuffle through them with my
        feet.
Then to one special spot I take
All I can gather with my rake,
Heaping them high above my head
To make a giant featherbed,
Where, when I climb on top to rest,
I sink into a cozy nest.

HELEN BARCLAY

AUTUMN MEMORIES

For my autumn memories
    I'll choose goldenrod,
A spray of purple asters,
    A fuzzy milkweed pod,
A dahlia proud and stately,
    A maple leaf so red,
A bunch of grapes, an apple,
    And a lowly teasel head.

LELAND B. JACOBS

IN AUTUMN

They're coming down in showers,
The leaves all gold and red;
They're covering the little flowers,
And tucking them in bed.
They've spread a fairy carpet
All up and down the street;
And when we skip along to school,
They rustle 'neath our feet.

WINIFRED C. MARSHALL

SONG FOR OCTOBER

I like the chill October nights,
    And bright October days,
I like the dancing bonfire lights
    And misty purple haze,

I like the boastful brigand breeze
That robs the meek, defenseless trees.

I like October's bright bouquet
    With sumac flares of red,
And goldenrod and asters gay
    In rich profusion spread.

No rival yet has nature planned
For fair October's wonderland.

LELAND B. JACOBS

OCTOBER LEAVES

"October leaves are falling fast,"
  I hear the people say;
"The autumn wind is tossing them,
  They must be swept away."

But *I* know they are fairy folk,
  These leaves, so gold and red,
Just having one last frolic,
  Before they go to bed.

        ELSIE M. FOWLER

AUTUMN

When the trees their summer splendor
  Change to raiment red and gold,
When the summer moon turns mellow
  And the night are getting cold;

When the squirrels hide their acorns,
  And the woodchucks disappear;
Then we know that it is autumn,
  Loveliest season of the year.

        CHARLOTTE L. RISER

OCTOBER

October is a gypsy queen
In dress of red and gold.
She sleeps beneath the silver moon
When nights are crisp and cold.

The meadows flame with color now,
Which once were cool and green.
Wild asters and the goldenrod
Bow low to greet their queen.

When she is tripping through the wood
With song so clear and sweet,
The autumn leaves come sifting down,
And rustle 'neath her feet.

        WINIFRED C. MARSHALL

AUTUMN IS A HAPPY TIME

The autumn is a happy time
With joyful colors everywhere,
With sunshine gleaming clear and
  bright,
And frosty odors on the air.

The trees have staged a masquerade—
In glowing colors nod and sway:
You'd hardly know Miss Maple now,
Or Mr. Poplar dressed so gay.

The goldenrod spreads sunny cheer
Upon the hillsides bleak and old;
The gentians and the asters blue
Still flaunt their beauty in the cold.

The autumn is a happy time
With white smoke trailing through
  the haze:
The earth's a colored picture book
That's full of joyful, gladsome ways.

        M. LUCILLE FORD

THE GARDEN CHORUS

If you would like to rise at dawn
  Some bright September day,
We should be pleased to have you
  come
  To hear our chorus play.

The string quartet is ready now,
  Composed of bumblebees;
They always play the violins,
  And hold them on their knees.

The clarinet is very sweet,
  And though from sight 'tis hid,
You will enjoy the solo by
  The gifted katydid.

We'll have to beg your pardon,
  though,
  About the big cornet;
The froggie practiced all night long,
  But isn't perfect yet.

We have a fine drum major, too;
  He wears a scarlet cap.
He's over in the maple tree,
  And beating time, tap, tap.

Besides, there is a set of chimes,
  That will delight you soon;
The canterbury bells are played
  On concert days at noon.

We hope you will come early, and
  Be sure to latch the gate.
The crickets take the tickets up,
  And cannot bear to wait.

        GERTRUDE M. JONES

AN AUTUMN DAY

Pumpkins in the cornfields,
  Gold among the brown,
Leaves of rust and scarlet
  Trembling slowly down;
Birds that travel southward,
  Lovely time to play;
Nothing is as pleasant
  As an autumn day!

        CARMEN LAGOS SIGNES

OCTOBER SOUNDS

Through the soft October air
  Nuts and leaves are falling;
In the woodland and everywhere
  Boys and girls are calling.

        ELEANOR CAMERON

A NIGHT IN OCTOBER

It's a night in October,
  As dark as can be.
I hear an owl hooting
  High up in a tree.

A witch on a broomstick
  Flies over the moon,
A gypsy is singing
  A gay lilting tune.

A big pumpkin lantern
  Grins down from a post.
Some black cats are chasing
  A clown and a ghost.

The doorbells are ringing,
  Though no one seems near.
Can you tell the reason
  For all this good cheer?

        WINIFRED C. MARSHALL

LADY NOVEMBER

The Lady with the cloak of brown
  Is walking on the hills.
She puts her baby seeds to bed
  And locks the brooks and rills.
The rustle of her silken skirt
  Is mingled with the rain,
And everywhere she goes, she sings,
  And this is the refrain:
"Good night, and glad good morning,
  My little children dear,
I'll tuck you in and bless you;
  'Tis bedtime of the year."

        PAULA BUTLER BOWMAN

HARVEST

The Harvest Queen came gently
And smilingly decreed,
"Come, every field, bring forth a yield
That's worthy of your seed."

The fertile earth responded
And heeded what she said.
The wheat fields gave abundantly
Their flour for man's bread.

The garden plots were lavish
With vegetables piled high
That gleamed in radiant colors
Beneath an autumn sky.

The orchards bent their branches
Their luscious fruits to share,
And nuts in autumn woodlands
Were showered freely there.

The Harvest Queen looked earthward
In proud and joyful mood.
The precious yield of farm and field
Would serve man's need for food.

LELAND B. JACOBS

AUTUMN MARKET

Every autumn in the woods,
    Falling leaves are burnished bright,
For in Fairy Markets there,
    Jack Frost holds a sale, each night.
Fairies hurry 'round to buy
    Crimson hose, a golden gown,
And, for study working clothes,
    Leaves are stained in shades of brown.

Then, beneath the big oak tree,
    Fairies shop for kitchen ware;
Polished copper frying pans,
    Pots and kettles are found there.
Autumn leaves the fairies use
    In so many ways, you see—
Dresses, rugs, and blankets, too,
    Even kettles for their tea!

FRANCES GORMAN RISSER

GOLDENROD

A blaze of yellow glory,
    The goldenrod in bloom;
Like a knight of olden story,
    It flaunts a feathery plume.

FANNIE MONTGOMERY

OCTOBER

October! October!
    There's magic in the name—
A clear sky, a blue sky,
    And sunsets all aflame.

October! October!
    It's harvest time again;
The high corn, the low corn,
    Is gathered in the bin.

October! October!
    Sing birds with open throats;
A long song, a last song,
    Of tender parting notes.

October! October!
    The hills are all aglow
With red leaves, and gold leaves,
    That dance when soft winds blow.

October! October!
    I love you more each year;
Your warm days, your soft days,
    To me they are most dear.

D. MAITLAND BUSHBY

JACK FROST

Little Jack Frost, who lives under the
    hill,
Last night came a-creeping, so softly
    and still,
        Right to our front door.
(It stayed tightly latched, and he rat-
    tled in vain.)
He left his white breath on our cold
    window pane.
        He's done it before!

Next morning my flowers looked
    faded and dead;
The trees' lovely leaves had turned
    yellow and red.
        (The trees proudly stood.)
Oh, I think that Jack Frost is a mar-
    velous elf
To paint leaves with colors from blos-
    soms himself.
        I wish that I could!

BERTHA REYNOLDS HUDELSON

THERE IS FROST IN THE AIR

There is frost in the air
And the boughs are all bare,
    And the asters have all left the
    hills.
There's wind in the trees,
And it's starting to freeze
    The dear little musical rills.

There is hint of a snow,
And wherever I go
    I see nature has stored up her
    seeds.
What they are I can't tell,
But she garners them well
    And will surely have all that she
    needs.

NONA KEEN DUFFY

AUTUMN

The asters and the goldenrod,
The downy silk of milkweed pod,
Along the roadsides far and near,
Remind us that the fall is here.
The grapes in purple clusters cling;
The little birds of southlands sing;
And fields and orchards give once
    more
Their rich and bounteous harvest
    store.
In flaming gowns the trees are
    dressed,
Until with whoop and merry jest,
The laughing wind in sportive play,
Blows all the dancing leaves away.
And now, all Nature at its best,
Prepares itself for winter rest.

BLANCHE CARTER BOWERS

JANUARY

Little January
   Tapped at my door today,
And said, "Put on your winter wraps,
   And come outdoors to play."

Little January
   Is always full of fun;
Today we coasted down the hill,
   Until the set of sun.

Little January
   Will stay a month with me
And we will have such jolly times—
   Just come along and see.

     WINIFRED C. MARSHALL

FEBRUARY

Oh, you may sing of bonny May
   And April's silver showers,
The red of gay October's leaves,
   Or August's fragrant flowers;

But give me jolly, crackling fires
   And snowflakes, soft and merry,
The month of holidays and fun,
   Gay, friendly February!

     FRANCES GORMAN RISSER

FIREWOOD

Sing a song of birchwood,
Cedar, oak and pine;
All the hearth is glowing bright,
All the room ashine.

Wind is in the chimney;
Snow is on the ground;
Kettle's singing very soft
With a cozy sound.

Sing a song of chestnut,
Hickory, and beech;
Firelight across the dark
As far as eye can reach.

Snow is on the forest;
The moon is icy cold;
But a lump of pitchwood
Will turn a room to gold.

     JULIA W. WOLFE

CRUMBS ON THE SNOW

When it's winter and the snow
Like a tablescloth is spread,
I remember hungry birds
And see that they are fed.
On their snowy tablecloth
They find my gift of bread.

     LUCRETIA PENNY

A CRYSTAL OF SNOW

A crystal of snow is a wonderful
   thing
With texture as fine as a butterfly's
   wing;
With network of atoms like filmy
   spun lace,
Or petal arrangement of fair flower
   face.

A crystal of snow is a beautiful thing
With the sparkle of drops that to
   spiders' webs cling
On a bright dewy morn; and the lus-
   ter of pearl;
Or a diamond gleam on a glistening
   curl.

A crystal of snow is a curious thing—
With dew of summer—or rain of
   spring—
And frost of autumn mixed into it all;
The flowers of cloudland that earth-
   ward do fall.

     M. LUCILLE FORD

WINTER NIGHT

Winter winds are blowing,
   Snow is drifting deep;
Cuddled under cover,
   Earth has gone to sleep.

Cozy in their houses
   Little children stay,
Where bright fires are burning
   To keep the cold away.

Snug in caves and burrows
   Wild things safe are curled,
While the feet of winter
   Tramp across the world.

     CLAUDE WEIMER

WINTER WRAPS

The pine tree wears a jaunty cap
   Of snowflakes white, today;
The fir tree wears a fluffy suit
   That makes him look quite gay;

The leafless maple, sheathed in ice,
   Is stylish as can be,
But I am snuggled in the coat
   My mother made for me!

     FRANCES GORMAN RISSER

THREE LITTLE OAK LEAVES

Three little oak leaves,
   Dressed in red and gold,
Waited on the oak tree
   For the winter's cold.

One made an elf a coat
   To keep him warm and snug,
One made a winter home
   For a chilly bug.

The third leaf fell softly
   Upon a seedling's bed—
The seed slept 'til springtime,
   Tucked in from toes to head!

     FRANCES GORMAN RISSER

WINTER PLEASURES

What a wealth of jolly things
Good old winter always brings!

Ice to skate on, hills to coast—
Don't know which we like the most!

Games to play, and corn to pop—
Midnight seems too soon to stop!

Books to read aloud at night,
Songs to sing, and plays to write!

Snow men built on starry nights,
Snow forts held in snowball fights!

High winds whirling drifted snow,
Breathes all frosty, cheeks aglow!

These and more, chill winter brings—
What a host of jolly things!

     NONA KEEN DUFFY

THE SNOWFLAKE

It floated very softly down,
  A little flake of snow,
As if it wondered where to light,
  And didn't really know.

And as it rested on the hedge,
  I thought of many things,
Of meadows that would soon be white,
  Of giant winds that sing,

Of wreaths with scarlet berries bright,
  Of Christmas trees aglow,
And all because it found our yard,
  That tiny flake of snow.

ALICE THORN FROST

PUZZLED

Oh, Jack Frost called on me last night
  And left an icy note
Upon my bedroom window, but
  I can't read what he wrote.
I hope he will come back again
  To call on me today
So I can ask him what he said
  Before it melts away.

MABEL NIEDERMEYER

FEBRUARY FUN

The snow man and the valentine
Are coming on the run;
As they draw near, they hear us cheer
For February fun.

The snow man and the valentine
Are standing here together,
Amid the snow and winds that blow
In February weather.

The snow man and the valentine
Are dancing up and down.
"Hooray!" they shout and dance
    about—
The snow man is a clown.

The snow man and the valentine
Are calling us to play.
"Come out! Come out!" they loudly
    shout,
And valentine is gay.

The snow man and the valentine
Are standing hand in hand.
They shout with glee for you and me
To share our winter land.

PHYLLIS MEAD

NOVEMBER WIND

Wind, wind, gallant and free,
Now you are bringing November to
    me!

    April and August
    And blossoming May,
    Each you have brought
    On your hurrying way.

    Each was so fair,
    I am certain 'tis true
    November will surely
    Be beautiful, too.

    Lovely as anything sweet
    That has flown,
    Full of delight
    In a way of its own.

Wind, wind, gallant and free,
Thank you for bringing November to
    me!

JOSEPHINE VAN DOLZEN PEASE

WINTERTIME

Late lies the wintry sun abed,
A frosty, fiery sleepyhead;
Blinks but an hour or two; and then,
A blood-red orange, sets again.

Before the stars have left the skies,
At morning in the dark I rise;
And shivering in my nakedness,
By the cold candle, bathe and dress.

Close by the jolly fire I sit
To warm my frozen bones a bit;
Or, with a reindeer-sled, explore
The colder countries round the door.

When to go out, my nurse doth wrap
Me in my comforter and cap;
The cold wind burns my face, and
    blows
Its frosty pepper up my nose.

Black are my steps on silver sod;
Thick blows my frosty breath abroad;
And tree and house, and hill and lake,
Are frosted like a wedding-cake.

ROBERT LOUIS STEVENSON

A WINTER GARDEN

I have a winter garden
Here on the window sill,
Where lovely flowers blossom,
Though days are dark and chill.

Each day I bring them water
And tend them with great care;
But it is worth the trouble
To have a garden there.

When fleecy, white snow blankets
Have covered other flowers,
I'll have my indoor garden
To cheer the winter hours.

WINIFRED C. MARSHALL

SPARKLING SNOW

The steps were covered,
The sidewalks were, too;
The roof tops were gone
Except for the flue;

The bushes were there,
Just humps on the ground;
The grass was certainly
Nowhere to be found;

The little twigs quivered
On each willow tree,
And swayed back and forth
And threw feathers at me.

The window was covered
With fluffy white flakes
Like frosting on one
Of my best birthday cakes.

O what a delight
To awaken today
And see sparkling white snow
In which to play.

HELEN KITCHELL EVANS

LET'S GO COASTING

Let us go coasting
  On my brand-new sled.

It is new and shiny;
  And is painted red!

It is big and roomy;
  We can ride it double.

Two can get on it
  Without any trouble.

You can help me pull it;
  We can ride together.

Let us go a coasting,
  For it's splendid weather!

Get your coat and mittens;
  All the world is white.

Let us go a-coasting
  While the snow is just right!

NONA KEEN DUFFY

OUT SKATING

We went to skate this afternoon—
  You know, we often do;
I wore my scarf and warmest coat,
  Fluff wore his fur coat, too.

But, oh, the wind was rough and rude,
  And blew my scarf about;
I'm sure it thinks it's fun to tease,
  Whenever I am out.

GERTRUDE M. ROBINSON

PETER,
THE SNOW MAN

It would not seem like winter,
  Without a snow man tall;
I've worked on one all morning,
  With Ted and little Paul.
This is a jolly snow man,
  With such a friendly smile,
We'll ask you out to meet him,
  In just a little while.

His hat belongs to Daddy,
  His button eyes are blue,
His bright red scarf and mittens
  Were knit by Cousin Sue.
We're going to call him Peter,
  We'd like to have him stay,
But sometime when we're all at school,
  He's sure to slip away.

WINIFRED C. MARSHALL

IN WINTER

I like to ride a coaster wagon;
  I like to roller-skate.
In summer I don't go to bed
  Till after half-past eight.

But I like winter best, I think
  When I can use my sled.
And then when I go skating, too,
  I'm tired enough for bed.

HAROLD EMERY

JOLLY SNOW MAN

We made a jolly snow man;
  You see, it snowed last night.

This afternoon the sun came out
  So very warm and bright,

We've had to touch him up a bit;
  His ears and nose were gone;

But now he's just as good as new,
  Out there upon the lawn.

He has a very cheery smile;
  I fear he does not know

That he will vanish some warm day,
  When sunshine melts the snow.

WINIFRED C. MARSHALL

OUR SNOW MAN

Our snow man's nearly finished,
  And we have had great fun;
Mother's coming out to look
  As soon as he is done.

His bright black eyes are bits of coal,
  His scarf belongs to Ted,
His hat's a sugar bucket
  We found out in the shed;

He has real buttons on his coat,
  A broomstick's in his hand;
He stands up very tall and straight,
  As though he owned the land.

WINIFRED C. MARSHALL

The Big Outdoors

YOURS AND MINE!

The sun, the trees, the grass, the sky,
The silver moon that's sailing by,
The rain and dew and snowflakes white,
The flowers sweet and stars of night!

The songs of birds, winds whispering,
The autumn leaves, the buds of spring—
Such lovely things to hear and see
Belong to you, belong to me!

FRANCES GORMAN RISSER

TULIPS

The tulips that bloom by the old
  garden wall
I play are fine ladies, all dressed for
  a ball.

Some wear fluffy ruffles of yellow or
  white,
While others wear crimson or orange
  so bright.

If they're caught in a shower on their
  way to the ball,
The rain does not hurt their silk
  dresses at all;

They're washed in dewdrops and
  dried in the sun;
To wear rainproof dresses, I think,
  must be fun.

WINIFRED C. MARSHALL

GAY TULIPS

Red and yellow tulips
  Standing up so straight
Brighten up the pathway,
  Leading to the gate.
And when breezes kiss them,
  Gracefully they sway,
Happy in the sunshine,
  Always looking gay.

MOLLIE B. HERMAN

SPRING'S HERALD

"I wonder," said the Crocus Bulb,
  "If it is time to grow:
It seems I've slept a long, long time
  Here in the ground below."

"I'm ready, too," said Daffodil,
  "To reach up toward the sun.
Come, let us go together—
  To go in two's is fun."

"You'd better wait and let me see,"
  The Pussy Willow said,
"If it is warm enough for you
  To venture on ahead.

"You're much too frail to take the
  risk,
  While I've a suit of fur;
If I should find that spring's returned
  I'll send you word to stir."

So Pussy climbed out on his branch,
  And then one bright spring day,
"Come up, the world's expecting you,"
  He telegraphed their way.

MABEL NIEDERMEYER

SPRING GARDEN

The small brown bulbs I planted
  Beside our garden wall
Now bloom, like Cinderellas,
  All ready for the ball.

In silken gowns attired,
  As pretty as you please,
Coquettishy they curtsy
  To every princely breeze.

LELAND B. JACOBS

PUSSY WILLOWS

On slender willow branches,
  In little coats of gray,
You sway in springtime's breezes
  Like kittens at their play.

Where do you stay all winter?
  Your ways are very queer,
But when I see you, Pussy,
  I know that spring is here!

MABEL F. HILL

WAKING UP

A little bean baby
Jumped out of bed,
With a white nightcap
Upon his wee head.

He yawned and stretched
In the warm, sunny air,
Till his cap tumbled off
His shiny green hair.

IRENE M. CROFOOT

CROCUS CHILDREN

Just a little crocus
  Growing in the grass
Can announce the springtime
  To the folks that pass.

Just a little maiden,
  And a laddie wee,
Can spread joy and sunshine
  Where they chance to be.

ALICE CROWELL HOFFMAN

DISAPPOINTMENT

My father has a catalogue,
A jolly flower catalogue,
With what he says are pictures of all
  the latest flowers—
Of pansy kitten faces,
And posies edged with laces,
And bells to ring for four o'clock but
  not the other hours.

I've studied Father's catalogue,
This latest flower catalogue,
I must confess I don't believe it's
  right up to the minute,
For I've hunted hours and hours
To find my favorite flowers,
And there's not a purple thistle or a
  dandelion in it!

LELAND B. JACOBS

OUR GARDEN'S FLOWER PARADE

Our garden's been having a flower parade,
And, oh, what a splendid exhibit they
  made.

The bluebells kept ringing the place
  and the date,
The marigolds beamed at the garden
  gate,
While the hollyhocks marched in a
  column straight
  In a dazzling flower parade.

The garden parade was, indeed, a delight
With daisies pirouetting in yellow
  and white,
And acrobat roses that climbed out of
  sight
To the top of the trellis with no sign
  of fright.
  What a thrilling flower parade!

Though I missed the bands and the
  music they played,
I stood quite entranced at the flower
  parade.

The pansies and I didn't move from
  our place,
And I knew from expressions on each
  pansy face
That they all approved of the delicate
  grace
  Of our garden's flower parade.

LELAND B. JACOBS

JACK'S SECRETS

Jack-in-the-Pulpit, straight and slim,
Said not a word when I spoke to him.
With the peak of his funny hood
  pulled low,
He just pretended he did not know
That three new violets, white and
  sweet,
Hid in the moss at his very feet.
There was fringed polygala up the
  trail;
A bluebird sat on an old fence rail;
A flicker looked from a hole in a tree;
He had a secret no one could see.
But Jack-in-the-Pulpit knew quite
  well
Why Bellwort tilted her long white
  bell,
What the brook was saying with
  whispering sound,
What sunbeams wrote on the velvet
  ground.
Oh, that sly little chap in the funny
  hood
Knew all the secrets up in the wood,
Though he stood so mute and straight
  and slim,
And said not a word when I spoke to
  him!

MABEL S. MERRILL

DANDELIONS

Last night a fairy strayed our way
  And played upon the lawn.
She danced and skipped from end to
  end—
  Then suddenly was gone.

What frightened her, I do not know,
  She dropped her purse and ran,
Leaving a wealth of golden coins
  To shine when day began!

HAZEL CEDERBORG

TINY SEEDS

Tiny seeds are everywhere
  Out of doors today.
Some have strong though airy wings
  To take them far away;
Some in cradles soft and brown,
From the trees to earth drop down,
Seeking for their winter's nap
  A soft, dark place to stay.

VERA L. STAFFORD

TULIPS

In the garden
  Tulips grow
Straight and golden
  In a row.
Each one holds its
  Empty cup
Drinking rain and
  Sunshine up.

V. W. LACHICOTTE

SPECIAL PRIVILEGE

My mother has a rosebush
Out by the garden gate.
Each day I count the buds on it—
Today I counted eight.
Tomorrow they'll be open,
All wide and sweet and pink;
And I may stand on tiptoe
And smell of them, I think.

DOROTHY H. GALLAGHER

THE HOLLYHOCK DOLLS

In grandmother's garden are hollyhocks tall
That sway in the breezes and peep
  o'er the wall;
And if you are lonesome, I know you
  can see
What wonderful playmates these
  blossoms can be,

For turn back their petals, and lo and
  behold!
Inside is a princess, a fairy we're
  told;
Just tie on a sash, leaving two petals
  clear
To make into sleeves—you've a dolly,
  my dear.

Oh, hollyhock ladies are dainty and
  fine,
All flounced and beruffled, they certainly shine;
And when they grow older and wither
  away,
They nod on their stems in the cheer-
  iest way.

MYRTLE BARBER CARPENTER

SEEDS

I planted shining seeds this spring—
  Just tiny seeds they seemed to be.
And yet I hoped so very much
  That they would change to flowers
  for me.

Today I saw a mist of green.
  It made me very happy, so
I said a little thank-you prayer
  To God, who made my flowers
  grow.

WINNIFRED J. MOTT

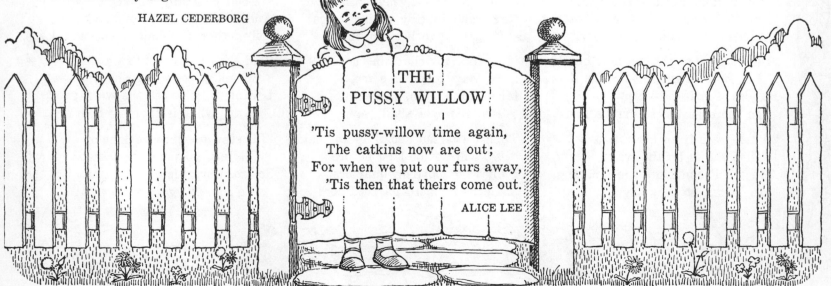

THE PUSSY WILLOW

'Tis pussy-willow time again,
  The catkins now are out;
For when we put our furs away,
  'Tis then that theirs come out.

ALICE LEE

A Tree Is Beautiful To See

A tree is beautiful to see,
When drenched with rain, its limbs
droop low,
Or when they're heaped with falling
snow
A tree is beautiful to see!

A tree is such a lovely sight,
When dressed in autumn red and gold,
Or when its first buds unfold—
A tree is such a lovely sight!

EDNA JEANNE GRAHAM

A tree is graceful, straight, and tall,
Outlined against the sunset sky,
Its leafy branches lifted high—
A tree is graceful, straight, and tall!

MY TREE

O Tree, so big and stout and strong,
You've lived so very, very long;
A hundred years or more, I'm told,
And yet you're not so very old.

A hundred secrets you could tell
Of children whom you love so well,
Who came and sat beneath your shade
Or underneath your branches played.

A hundred birds have built their
nests;
Your leaves have softly kissed their
breasts;
Your branches seem to touch the sky,
Yet you were once as small as I.

Some day when I have grown up, too,
I'm coming back to visit you;
And changed though other things will
be,
I'll find the same dear friendly tree.

GARNET ENGLE

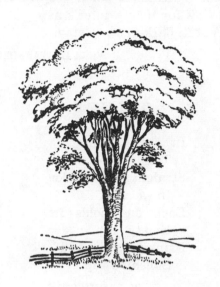

A QUEER TWIG

Out in the woods I found today
    A queer thing, without doubt—
A wee twig that did not stay still,
    But tried to walk about.

I thought this tiny twig had planned
    To play a funny trick,
Until I learned it was a bug
    Known as the "walking stick."

ALICE CROWELL HOFFMAN

THE LADIES

In their gowns of silver,
    With parasols of green,

The ladies have gone walking
    In a pleasant scene.

Graceful is their bearing
    And gracefully they go,

With low-toned chat and comment,
    In a friendly row.

Sunbeams, golden-tinted,
    Before them touch the ground;

Their silken gowns in rustling
    Make a whispering sound.

I can see them strolling
    As from the road I look—

Six ladies who are really
    White birches by a brook!

ARTHUR WALLACE PEACH

THE GOSSIP OF THE NUTS

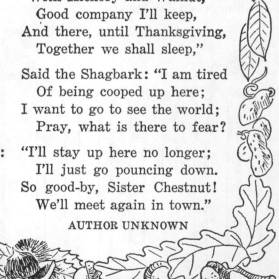

Said the Shagbark to the Chestnut,
    "Is it time to leave the bur?"
"I don't know," replied the Chestnut,
    "There's Hazelnut—ask her."

"I don't dare to pop my nose out,
    Till Jack Frost unlocks the door,
Besides, I'm in no hurry
    To increase the squirrel's store.

"A telegram from Peanut says
    That she is on the way;
And the Pecan Nuts are ripening,
    In Texas, so they say."

Just here the little Beechnut,
    In his three-cornered hat,
Remarked in tiny piping voice:
    "I'm glad to hear of that;

"For then my charming cousin
    So very much like me,
Miss Chinquapin, will come
    And happy I shall be."

Then Butternut spoke up and said:
    " 'Twill not be long before
I'll have to move my quarters
    To the farmer's garret floor;

"With Hickory and Walnut,
    Good company I'll keep,
And there, until Thanksgiving,
    Together we shall sleep,"

Said the Shagbark: "I am tired
    Of being cooped up here;
I want to go to see the world;
    Pray, what is there to fear?

"I'll stay up here no longer;
    I'll just go pouncing down.
So good-by, Sister Chestnut!
    We'll meet again in town."

AUTHOR UNKNOWN

A PATH FRIEND

I know a little path
　　Who always seems to be
Quite ready to go walking
　　On pleasant days with me.

Sometimes, he walks along
　　Beside me as I go,
Then scampers on to vanish,
　　But where I do not know.

Around some woodland curve,
　　Or where the thickets stand
He slips from me while waving
　　A gay and merry hand.

Sometimes among the ferns
　　He hides himself from view,
Then pops out as I'm passing
　　And shouts a joyous "Boo!"

I like to stroll with him
　　On sunny, summer days;
He is a cheery comrade
　　With happy, friendly ways!

ARTHUR WALLACE PEACH

FOREST FIRES

Someone dropped a burning match
　　Unheeded by the way;
It caught on fire some underbrush;
　　Its user did not stay.
From grass to brush, from brush to
　　tree,
　　So stealthily it ran,
That no one ever guessed or knew
　　Just where that fire began.

Someone built a campfire
　　And failed to put it out.
A breeze came up and quickened;
　　The embers spread about;
And soon the woods were blazing.
　　The fire spread and spread;
The trees that took long years to
　　grow
　　Stand blackened now and dead.

Someone saw a little fire
　　As he was passing by.
He did not stop to put it out;
　　He did not even try.
He had not started it, of course;
　　He had no time to spare;
That it might start a forest fire
　　He did not even care.

MYRTLE BARBER CARPENTER

A HIKING CAUTION

Come let us hike, come let us roam,
But let's not leave our eyes at home.

All out-of-doors is overflowing
With things to see while we are going.

Gay birds on wing, and nests in trees;
Grasshoppers, too, and velvet bees.

Wild flowers fair and crawling creatures
That can indeed become our teachers.

Oh, let's be sure we're wide awake
The next time that a hike we take!

ALICE CROWELL HOFFMAN

THE LITTLE BROWN ROAD

The little brown road
　　That goes running along
Seems to be humming
　　A holiday song.

It sings of the brooklet
　　Where speckled trout splash,
Of gay flowery meadows
　　Where butterflies flash.

"Come race me," it teases,
　　And darts up a hill;
I think I could catch it
　　If it would stand still.

DONOVAN MARSHALL

ROAD SONG

A winding road, a side road
　　Beckons and nods to me
It may go to the mountain,
　　It may go to the sea;
But I must heed a summons
　　That cannot be denied.
I must know where the road goes
And what's on the other side.

ALICE CROWELL HOFFMAN

THE ROAD

When we go riding into town,
The road goes up and the road goes
　　down;

Round a corner where a sign says
　　SLOW!
Over a bridge with the water below.

I like to watch the trees and sky
And the houses and barns that we go
　　by;

I like the horses and pigs and sheep
And the cows that all the farmers
　　keep;

But best of all is to look behind
And watch the road unwind and un-
　　wind.

I always think and I always say,
"Where does the road run when it
　　runs away?"

REBA MAHAN STEVENS

AIRY PRESENTS

The wind is giving presents
   To all his friends today.
He gives the lake some ripples
   Of lacy silver spray;

He gives the trees a rustle
   To play with all day long;
And every little chimney nook
   Receives a jolly song;

He's building castles in the clouds,
   Much to the sun's delight;
Perhaps he'll give the moon a wreath
   Of clouds to wear all night!

FRANCES GORMAN RISSER

SONG OF THE NORTH WIND

I am here from the North, the frozen
   North,—
   'Tis a thousand leagues away,—
And I left, as I came from my cavern
   forth,
   The streaming lights at play.

From the deep sea's verge to the ze-
   nith high
   At one vast leap they flew,
And kindled a blaze in the midnight
   sky
   O'er the glittering icebergs blue.

The frolicsome waves they shouted to
   me,
   As I hurriedly over them passed,
"Where are the chains that can fetter
   the sea?"
   But I bound the boasters fast.

In their pride of strength the pine-
   trees tall
   Of my coming took no heed;
But I bowed the proudest of them all
   As if it had been a reed.

AUTHOR UNKOWN

THE WIND IN A FROLIC

The wind one morning sprang up
   from sleep,
Saying, "Now for a frolic! now for a
   leap!
Now for a madcap, galloping chase!
I'll make a commotion in every
   place!"

So it swept with a bustle right
   through a great town,
Creaking the signs, and scattering
   down
The shutters, and whisking, with
   merciless squalls,
Old women's bonnets and gingerbread
   stalls.
There never was heard an angrier
   shout
As the apples and oranges tumbled
   about;

Then away to the fields it went blustering and humming,
And the cattle all wondered whatever
   was coming.
It plucked by their tails the grave ma-
   tronly cows,
And tossed the colts' manes all about
   their brows,
Till offended at such a familiar salute,
They all turned their backs and stood
   silently mute.

Through the forest it roared, and
   cried gayly, "Now,
You sturdy old oaks, I'll make you
   bow!"
It made them bow without more ado,
Or it cracked their great branches
   through and through.

Then it rushed like a monster o'er cottage and farm,
Striking their inmates with sudden
   alarm;
And they ran out like bees in a mid-
   summer swarm.
There was rearing of ladders, and
   logs laying on,
Where the thatch from the roof
   threatened soon to be gone.

But the wind had passed on, and had
   met in a lane
With a schoolboy, who panted and
   struggled in vain,
For it tossed him, and twirled him,
   then passed laughing by
To turn and to snatch at his cap on
   the sly.

WILLIAM HOWITT

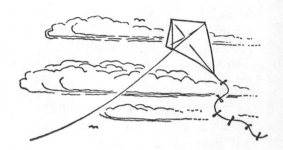

WHO LIKES THE WIND?

"I," said the kite,
"I like the wind,
I call it fun
To travel high and wink at the sun!"

"I," said the boat,
"I like the wind,
Just let it blow
And fill my sails and away I'll go!"

"I," said the thistle,
"I like the wind,
I call it fun
To leap and jump and before the wind
   run!"

LEAH GIBBS KNOBBE

MY PLAYMATE

I have an outdoor playmate
   Who's as jolly as can be;
Sometimes I'm sure he's hiding
   Up in our apple tree,
For the green leaves nod and rustle
   And seem to wave at me.

In springtime when we're playing,
   He is so very spry;
He catches up my paper kite
   And carries it up high
Above the tops of houses
   With their chimneys in the sky.

He often blows and whistles
   For me to come outside,
Then when I'm on my scooter
   He pushes while I ride—
And yet I've never seen him
   Though I've tried and tried and
     tried.

MABEL NIEDERMEYER

THE WRESTLER

The wind came roaring into town.
He hurled great boughs into the
      street
And thumped upon my windowpane
And kicked my door with angry feet.

He whistled through his teeth and
      howled:
"Come out and fight! Come out and
      fight!"
Then jumped upon a dooryard pine
And wrestled with it all the night.

HERBERT ELLIOTT

I LIKE THE WIND

I like the wind
Which I cannot see;
I like the things it does for me—
It blows the snow against my face;
It makes me want to run a race;
But in the spring it's like soft lace
And blows sweet odors in my face.
I like the wind
Which I cannot see—
I like the things it teaches me!

M. LOUISE C. HASTINGS

WINDY NIGHTS

Whenever the moon and stars are set,
   Whenever the wind is high,
All night long in the dark and wet,
   A man goes riding by.
Late in the night when the fires are
      out,
Why does he gallop and gallop about?

Whenever the trees are crying aloud,
   And ships are tossed at sea,
By, on the highway, low and loud,
   By at the gallop goes he,
By at the gallop he goes, and then
By he comes back at the gallop again.

ROBERT LOUIS STEVENSON

WIND

The wind blows high,
   The wind blows low,
I wonder where
   It means to go?
Just now it turned
   Around, around,
As did cart wheels
   Upon the ground;
Then with a great
   Big angry pout
Turned my umbrella
   Inside out!
The wind blows high,
   The wind blows low,
I wonder where
   It means to go?

VIRGINIA W. LACHICOTTE

THE WIND WIZARD

The wind must be a wizard;
   He can do so many things.
Although he is invisible,
   He has more power than kings.

He moves the clouds across the sky—
   Whole fleets of them—like ships;
He chops the waters of the sea
   Into small white chips.

Great trees bow low before his breath
   As do the blades of grass,
For he can break a tree as if
   It were made of brittle glass.

And when he's in a gentle mood,
   He nibbles fields like sheep,
Plays soft, low music in the grass,
   Or cuddles down to sleep.

MARION DOYLE

SMOKE

A puff of blue smoke
Like a great big feather
Curls out of our chimney
In cold wintry weather—
A feather *some* giant
Might like to wear
Stuck up in his hat,
To town or the fair!

IDA TYSON WAGNER

THE WIND'S LULLABY

Sometimes the wind is a bluff old fellow
Who hurries by with roar and bellow;
But sometimes where a wee nest swings,
He sways it gently and then he sings:
   "Softly I rock you, wee little nest;
   Hush, little birdlings, slumber and
      rest:
   Hush-a-by low, hush-a-by slow,
   By-low."

High in the elms, in the maple trees lofty,
Where twilight shadows gather softly,
And smiles through leaves a mother moon,
He sings a tender, sleepy tune:
   "Gently I rock you, wee little nest;
   Hush little birdies, slumber is best:
   Hush-a-by slow, hush-a-by low,
   By-low."

Sometimes the wind is a gruff old fellow
Who likes to shout and roar and bellow,
But sometimes in the evening long
He sings a sleepy, slumber song!

ARTHUR WALLACE PEACH

THE WIND

I saw you toss the kites on high
And blow the birds about the sky;
And all around I heard you pass,
Like ladies' skirts across the grass—
   O wind, a-blowing all day long,
   O wind, that sings so loud a song!

I saw the different things you did,
But always you yourself you hid.
I felt you push, I heard you call,
I could not see yourself at all—
   O wind, a-blowing all day long,
   O wind, that sings so loud a song!

O you that are so strong and cold,
O blower, are you young or old?
Are you a beast of field and tree,
Or just a stronger child than me?
   O wind, a-blowing all day long,
   O wind, that sings so loud a song!

ROBERT LOUIS STEVENSON

SEA SHELLS

Hold a shell up to your ear
To hear the fairies sing
Their jolly, humming melodies
That have a happy ring,

Telling of the ships that sail
Across the ocean blue,
About the mermaids and the whales,
And what the fishes do!

Fairies in their sea-shell homes
Are such a merry crew;
If you will listen at their door
They all will sing to you!

ETHEL HAWTHORNE TEWKSBURY

AT THE SEASIDE

When I was down beside the sea
A wooden spade they gave to me
 To dig the sandy shore.

My holes were empty like a cup
In every hole the sea came up,
 Till it could come no more.

ROBERT LOUIS STEVENSON

A WAVE

I sat on the beach and a beautiful
 wave
 Came tumbling right up to me.
It threw some pink shells on the sand
 at my feet,
 Then hurried straight back out to
 sea.

It ran away swiftly and leaped up in
 foam;
 It bumped other waves in its glee.
I think it was hurrying to gather
 more shells,
 To bring as a present for me.

GUSSIE OSBORNE

SONG OF A SHELL

I held a sea shell to my ear,
 And listened to its tale
Of vessels bounding o'er the main
 And all the ships that sail.
It sang of brilliant water flowers—
 The bright anemones
That bloom beneath the ocean
 waves—
 Tossed in from seven seas.

Each time I harken to this song,
 I hear the breakers moan,
And fancy that a warning bell
 Rings from a lighthouse lone.
No longer need I wish to go
 Where foam-capped billows swell,
For I've an ocean of my own
 Within this pearly shell.

VIOLET L. CUSLIDGE

GREAT LAKES STORM

How wild the lake!
How wild and gray!
The whitecaps leap
In spume and spray.
Unharnessed winds
Make billows roar.
They rush and break,
The skies grow black,
Sharp lightning strikes,
Loud thunders crack—
Now guard the dikes!
Down sweeps the rain,
A blinding sheet!
High combers dash—
Sky, water meet.
The storm is spent—
Forth peeps the sun.
White-crested waves
Rush, break, and run.
Though skies may clear,
Swells roll all day.
Seagulls appear,
Sun gilds the bay.

LOUISE M. DIEHL

THE WAVES

The little waves ran up the sand,
 All rippling, bright and gay.
But they were little robbers,
 For they stole the sand away,
And when they'd tossed it all about,
 They piled it in the bay.

One day, there came a clever man;
 He walked along the shore,
And when he saw the crested waves
 Creep higher than before,
Said he, "I'll build a harbor wall,
 And you'll come here no more."

So then he started working;
 Stone after stone he brought.
The little waves beat at the wall;
 By day and night they fought,
Their white hair streaming in the
 wind,
 Their manner quite distraught.

But when the wall was finished,
 Like other of their ilk,
They tiptoed round the harbor
 As sleek and smooth as silk,
And purred around the fishing boats,
 Like kittens lapping milk.

GERTRUDE M. JONES

FOG

When I went out this morning,
 The world was veiled in gray;
Fog, like a silver blanket,
 Was wrapped around the day;

There wasn't any sunshine,
 And when I looked to see,
I couldn't find the bushes,
 The fence, or big oak tree.

It was a funny, blurry world,
 Full of strange shapes and places,
With people's voices all about,
 But not a sign of faces.

It was like walking in a cloud—
 I almost lost my way;
A fog is fun, but I am glad
 It never comes to stay!

FRANCES GORMAN RISSER

NATURE'S MUSIC

It's going to rain soon,
And how do I know?
Why, all of the fireflies
Are ceasing to glow;

The crickets are quiet,
And so are the trees;
The whole world is hushed,
There's not even a breeze;

It's just like an audience,
Very polite,
That hopes to enjoy
Good rain music tonight.

MARIAN STEARNS CURRY

THE RAIN MOON

Grandma says the rain moon
Hangs its horns straight down,
Spilling all the water out,
Raining on the town.

Grandma says a dry moon's
Shaped just like a cup,
Keeping all the water in,
Holding it straight up.

Wish we'd have a rain moon
When I go to bed;
I like to hear the raindrops
Patter overhead.

Wish we'd have a dry moon
When I want to play.
Please, Mr. Moon Man,
Turn it round that way.

EDNA L. DAILY

THUNDER

Do you know what thunder is
Up in the sky so gray?
It's raindrops carelessly slamming
    doors
As they run out to play.

MARIAN STEARNS CURRY

SECRETS

Ho, raindrops that patter
And whisper and chatter,
Please, what are you talking about?
"We are talking of April,
And buds on the maple,
And when the first flowers come out;
Of wee grasses springing,
And robins a-winging,
And children that frolic and shout;
Of blue skies and nestlings—
Are these not the best things
That raindrops *could* whisper about?"

BERTHA F. ROSS

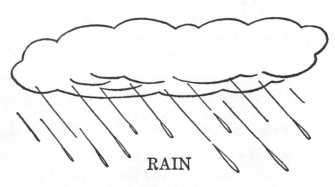

RAIN

The rain is raining all around,
    It falls on field and tree,
It rains on the umbrellas here,
    And on the ships at sea.

ROBERT LOUIS STEVENSON

THE DANCE
OF THE RAINDROPS

The raindrops are having a dance,
    heigh-ho!
  I wish we might join them don't
    you?
The frog ponds and puddles make
    excellent floors;
  Of these they can boast quite a few.

The orchestra, high in the old oak
    tree,
  Leaf instruments play with such
    skill,
Their pit-patty music refreshing and
    gay
  Makes it hard for our feet to keep
    still.

So if your sky is cloudy and gray
  Why worry and hang down your
    head?
Just heed the gay call at your own
    windowpane
  And dance with the raindrops, in-
    stead.

NANCY FRITZ MOON

SINGING RAIN

This morning very early,
    While I was still in bed,
I heard the patter, patter,
    Of the rain from overhead.

It came as if to wake me;
    I think it seemed to say,
"Wake up, and see me splashing!
    Here is another day."

The rain is always singing songs,
    Of thirsty flower or tree,
And by and by it is a brook,
    And travels toward the sea.

WYROA HANSEN

DEW

This morning when I went to walk,
    The shining dew was on the grass;

It sparkled on each slender blade
    Like tiny little beads of glass.

And later, when the sun was high,
    I took my scooter out to play.

The grass was dry; I think the sun
    Had wiped the dewdrops all away.

IRENE B. CROFOOT

RAIN SONG

Flowers are blowing
    In the breeze.
Wind is bending
    All the trees.
Sun is hiding,
    This cool day.
Clouds are gathering
    On the way.
Rain is coming
    Soon and long.
Nature's singing
    A rain song.

DOROTHY W. REILLY

SILVER WORLD

The trees are trimmed in silver glass,
  The earth is silver, too,
A silver moon hangs high above
  In skies of silver blue;

I tiptoe out so carefully
  Into the frosty air,
And look about for winter elves—
  I know they must be there.

I cannot see a fairy,
  But I hear a tinkly sound,
And then a little silver twig
  Comes tumbling to the ground;

I know that they are hiding
  In trees so silver bright,
And planning frosty scenes to paint
  On windowpanes tonight!

FRANCES GORMAN RISSER

THE SUN'S TRAVELS

The sun is not a-bed, when I
At night upon my pillow lie;
Still round the earth his way he takes,
And morning after morning makes.

While here at home, in shining day,
We round the sunny garden play,
Each little Indian sleepy-head
Is being kissed and put to bed.

And when at eve I rise from tea,
Day dawns beyond the Atlantic Sea;
And all the children in the West
Are getting up and being dressed.

ROBERT LOUIS STEVENSON

THE NIGHT SKY

When at night I've gone to bed,
With stars a-twinkling overhead,
Lots of things I think about
As I watch them peeping out.

Do the smallest stars all play
Out there on the Milky Way?
When they're thirsty do you think
From the Dipper they might drink?

Are the little stars up there
Frightened when they see the Bear?
I am sure he wouldn't bite,

For I watch him every night,
And his picture in my book
Has a kind and friendly look.

Lots of others are up there
Far above me in the air.
Sometimes I can find the Lion
And the Dog of good Orion.

It's such fun to see them all,
Winter, summer, spring, and fall;
One by one I watch them peep
Till at last I fall asleep.

CLARA BELL THURSTON

SWINGING ON THE MOON

Oh, come, go swinging on the moon;
  We'll watch the stars spin 'round
    and 'round,
And while we're swinging on the
    moon,
  We'll see the hills go up and down.

What makes the hills go up and down
  And never, never run away?
One side goes up and one goes down
  Because the hills are made that
    way.

Oh, come, go swinging while we may,
  The smiling moon is bending low,
And we'll be gone 'til break of day
  And swinging, swinging, swinging
    go.

BESS STOUT LAMBERT

A SPRINKLING POT

I know a large white sprinkling pot,
  So big that when it sprinkles
Over fields and over woods
  The dropping water twinkles.

When we take a sprinkling pot
  To water thirsty flowers
We must sprinkle here and there
  Among the garden bowers.

But the sprinkling pot I know
  Sends the bright drops falling
Over gardens, over fields,
  Where thirsty land is calling.

The sprinkling pot I have in mind
  You often can see sprinkling—
A rainy cloud on rainy days
  That sends the raindrops twinkling.

ARTHUR WALLACE PEACH

WATER IS A LOVELY THING

Water is a lovely thing—
Dark and ripply in a spring,
Dark and quiet in a pool,
In a puddle brown and cool;
In the river blue and gray,
In a raindrop silver gray,
In a fountain crystal bright;
In a pitcher frosty cold,
In a bubble pink and gold;
In a happy summer sea
Just as green as green can be;
In a rainbow far unfurled,
Every color in the world;
All the year from spring to spring,
Water is a lovely thing.

JULIA W. WOLFE

MORNING SONG

One fine morning, very early,
  When the little birds awoke
All the world was bright with dia-
    monds
  Dropped from Mother Nature's
    cloak.

Every daisy had a necklace,
  Every grass blade wore a ring,
And the wild rose held a mirror
  For the butterfly's bright wing.

AGNES M. SCHABERG

THE MOON

The moon has a face like the clock
  in the hall;
She shines on thieves on the garden
  wall,
On streets and fields and harbor
  quays,
And birdies asleep in the forks of
  the trees.
The squalling cat and the squeaking
  mouse,
The howling dog by the door of the
  house,
The bat that lies in bed at noon,
All love to be out by the light of the
  moon.
But all the things that belong to
  the day
Cuddle to sleep to be out of her way;
And flowers and children close their
  eyes
Till up in the morning the sun shall
  arise.

ROBERT LOUIS STEVENSON

A PINE-TREE PUMPKIN

Whoever saw, you say to me,
  This strangest sight of all,
A golden pumpkin growing
  On a pine tree tall?

A pumpkin yellow, big and round,
  Right on a pine-tree branch,
So clear that you, on looking,
  Could see it at a glance!

But when at night you see the moon
  Behind a dark pine tree,
Just use your fancy and you'll find
  The pumpkin that I see!

ARTHUR WALLACE PEACH

THE LADY MOON

Lady Moon, Lady Moon, where do you
    sail?
  Over the roof, over the town, over
    hill, over dale?
Look down on the children asleep in
    their beds,
  And see on the pillows the dear
    little heads.
Do you bring them sweet dreams,
    Lady Moon?

Lady Moon, Lady Moon, why do you
    smile
  As you silently traverse each long,
    starlit mile?
Are you thinking of dreams that
    danced through your head
  As you slept snug and warm in
    your own little bed?
Oh, what were your dreams, Lady
    Moon?

Lady Moon, Lady Moon, sailing up
    high
Watch over all children so quiet in
    sleep;
  Bring smiles to their faces and
    cause none to weep.
Oh, bring them sweet dreams, Lady
    Moon!

HELEN CARSON JANSSEN

AT EVENING

I like the little sleepy sounds
  You hear when day is done
When shadows gather here and there
  At setting of the sun.

A brook grows drowsy in the eve,
  As dusk comes still and slow;
You hear across the quiet night
  His murmur soft and low.

The wind no longer calls and shouts
  From high up in the trees;
He hums, instead, through evening
    hours
  His lulling melodies.

And little leaves that talk all day
  With wind and flitting birds
Speak now among the darkened
    boughs
  Their gentle whispering words.

So as the hours of sunset come
  And daytime noises cease,
The evening brings the weary world
  Its gifts of dreams and peace!

ARTHUR WALLACE PEACH

MOON MIRROR

The moon's a silver mirror
  Hung in the heavens fair,
So that the vain star maidens
  Can smooth their shining hair.

On cloudy nights, the mirror's gone,
  And stars stay out of sight,
They say: "My dear, I can't appear,
  My hair—it is a sight!"

FRANCES GORMAN RISSER

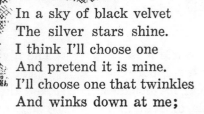

MY STAR

In a sky of black velvet
The silver stars shine.
I think I'll choose one
And pretend it is mine.
I'll choose one that twinkles
And winks down at me;

Then snug in my bed every
Night I shall see
My very own star shining
Far overhead,
And winking good night to me,
Curled up in bed.

MARION KENNEDY

TREE SHADOWS

I did not know how rare a sight
    A tree could be,
Until I spent a summer month
    Down by the sea.
On either side the sandy dunes
    The waves ran free,
And islands with white lighthouses
    Adorned the sea.
But when the sun's glare tired my
    eyes,
    I could not flee:
There were no grateful shadows made
    By leafy tree.
So now I dread to break a branch
    Grown by a tree,
Because I know how rare a sight
    Green shade may be.

             LUCY M. CHURCH

TOUCHING THE SKY

If I were on the tiptop branch
    Of that tall maple tree,
I'd reach right up and touch the sky,
And wrap a cloud round me.

I'd take a cloud all smooth and white
    To be my sailing boat,
I'd dip my hands in foamy clouds,
    And through the sky I'd float.

             LYDIA LION ROBERTS

STRANGE AIRSHIPS

The seeds are spreading their gauzy
    wings
    As light as feather down,
And floating off upon the wind
    That blows throughout the town.

Some others in their cradles rock
    Upon the trees so high,
And when the Frost King gives the
    sign,
    To newer homes they'll fly.

The burs are fairy airships
    Which flower pilots guide;
They seek new hangars for their
    planes
    In places far and wide.

Of all the man-made ships we see,
    Though wonderful, 'tis true,
Not one is half so marvelous,
    Wee seed airships, as you.

        MYRTLE BARBER CARPENTER

Spring Is Near

It is pleasant to think, just under the
    snow,
    That stretches so bleak and cold,
Are beauty and warmth that we can-
    not know,
    Green leaves and blossoms gold.

Yes, under this frozen and dumb ex-
    panse,
    Ungladdened by bee or bird or flow-
    er,
A world where the leaping fountains
    glance,
    And the buds expand, is waiting
    the hour.

It is hidden now; not a glimmer
    breaks
    Through the hard blue ice and the
    sparkling drift.
The world shrinks back from the
    downy flakes
    Which out of the fold of the night-
    cloud sift.

But as fair and real a world it is
    As any that rolls in the upper blue;
If you wait you will hear its melodies,
    And see the sparkle of fount and
    dew.

And often now when the skies are
    wild,
    And hoarse and sullen the night
    winds blow,
And lanes and hollows with drifts are
    piled,
    I think of the violets under the
    snow;

I look in the wild-flower's tremulous
    eye,
    I hear the chirp of the groundbird
    brown;
A breath from the budding grove
    steals by,
    And the swallows are dipping
    above the lawn.

So there, from the outer sense con-
    cealed,
    It lies, shut in by a veil of snow;
But there, to the inward eye revealed,
    Are boughs that blossom and flow-
    ers that glow.

The lily shines on its bending stem,
    The crocus opens its April gold,
And the rose up-tosses its diadem
    Against the floor of the winter's
    cold.   FAY HEMPSTEAD

Birds and

Animals

CONVERSATION

Cackle, gobble, quack, and crow,
Neigh and bray and bleat and low,
Twitter, chirrup, cheep, and coo,
Bark and growl and purr and mew.

Humming, buzzing, hiss, and sting,
Hoot and cockoo, caw and sing,
Squeal and grunt and snort and
   squawk;
Who said, "Only people talk"?

ALETHA M. BONNER

33

THE CARPENTER BIRD

If I could choose
Of all the birds
   The bird I'd like to be,
I'd choose to be a woodpecker
  And work on the trunk of a tree.

I'd rap-a-tap-tap
And I'd hammer away,
   For a carpenter I'd be
If I could choose
Of all the birds
   The bird I'd like to be!

M. LOUISE C. HASTINGS

FEEDING THE BIRDS

In northern lands, long, long ago,
  So wrapped in ice and sleet—
Where spring came tardily and slow,
  And birds could find no food to eat,
Then good folk often would bestow
  On them a sheaf of wheat.
Those feathered friends were glad, I
   know,
  And so I think we should repeat
This kindly act when winter comes,
And give the birds some grain or
   crumbs.

MARGARET E. BRUNER

CHICKADEES

We saved some lumps of suet
  And tied them on a tree
That stood quite close to our side
   porch
  Where we could plainly see.

The antics of the hungry birds
  Filled us with great delight,
And soon we found the chickadees
  Were much the gayest sight.

For they didn't keep still a minute;
  They teetered, hopped, and swung.
Upside down they pecked the lumps
  As to little twigs they clung.

We laughed at their amusing tricks;
  Then clapped our hands in glee,
For they began to sing their thanks—
  Gay "Chick-a-dee, dee-dee."

CLARA G. CORNELL

AN EASY WAY

Birds slip away without good-by's,
  When south they go in fall.
They never have to pack a thing;
  Just up and fly—that's all.

NORMAN C. SCHLICHTER

BIRD SUITS

Gay is the suit that the robin wears,
  Proud of his vest is he,
And he sticks out his chest as he sings
   in the crest
  Of his favorite apple tree.

Gaudily bright is the blue jay's dress,
  Haughtily does he stand
On a maple tree limb where all can see
   him
  As he shouts to his noisy band.

Orange and black the oriole wears,
  Flashing among the trees;
He looks like a flame as he flies with
   sure aim
  To his nest where it sways with the
   breeze.

Brown is the dress that the wood
   thrush wears,
  Modest and neat and prim,
But her song I love best when the
   sun's in the west
  And the world with the twilight
   is dim!

ARTHUR WALLACE PEACH

ROBIN

Dull coat and rosy breast,
  Robin, will you be my guest?

You shall have our greenest tree
  For your nestling family,

And when summer fruits are due,
  You shall have some cherries, too!

Dull coat and rosy breast,
  Robin, will you be my guest?

ELEANOR HALBROOK ZIMMERMAN

A GAY CHICKADEE

A gay little, gray little bird one day,
When all the world under heavy snow
   lay,
Came flying right down to my
   window sill
And pecked at the pane with his
   sharp little bill.

"Chick-a-dee-dee, dee-deem dee-dee,"
My small feathered visitor said to me.
And I think he was telling as best he
   was able
That the snow had covered his dinner
   table.

So I scattered some raisins and seeds
   on the sill,
Right where he could peck till he'd
   eaten his fill.
I was glad I could pay the gay chick-
   adee
For devouring the bugs on our big
   apple tree.

CLARA G. CORNELL

LITTLE GRAY PIGEON

A little gray pigeon, with little pink
   feet,
And fluttery tail and wings,
Walks over our lawn, and sits on our
   roof,
And most of the time he sings.

He has rings on his neck that shine
   in the sun,
And he ruffles them when he walks;
I wish I could hold him and see how
   he sings;
I believe I could teach him to talk.

FRANCES ARNOLD GREENWOOD

TWO BABY OWLS

Two baby owls sat in a tree,
And blinked because they could not
    see.
"The sun is shining bright," they
    said,
"So let's go home and go to bed."

A little squirrel frisking near
The owls was very quick to hear.
Said he, "It's fine for work or play;
I'm glad the sun shines bright to-
    day."

ADA CLARK

MR. OWL

I saw an owl up in a tree,
I looked at him, he looked at me;
I couldn't tell you of his size,
For all I saw were two big eyes;
As soon as I could make a dash,
Straight home I ran, quick as a flash!

EDNA HAMILTON

THE STERN OLD OWL

A stern old owl sat in a tree,
    In a tree, in a tree,
And wide awake all night was he,
    Without one wink.

He saw two rabbits hurry past,
    Flurry past, furry, fast;
He heard a woodchuck scurry past,
    And one brown mink.

But when some elves came whirling
    through,
    Curling through, twirling through,
"To-whoo," said he, "to-whit, to-
    whoo!"
    Blink, blink, blink.

NANCY BYRD TURNER

THE OWL AND THE WIND

Oh, did you hear the wind last night
    A-blowing right at you?
It sounded just as though it said,
    "Oooo—ooo—oooo!"

The wind now has a playmate,
    Just as most children do,
He sits up in a tree and hoots,
    "To-whoo, to-whit, to-whoo."

So when you hear the owl and wind
    Just at the close of day,
They're calling to each other
    To come out now and play.

MADELINE A. CHAFFEE

BIRDS AND ANIMALS

THE MERRY LAMB

"Little Lamb, come here and say
What you're doing all the day?"

"Long, long before you wake
Breakfast I am glad to take,
In the meadow eating up
Daisy, cowslip, buttercup.

Then about the fields I play,
Frisk and scamper all the day:
When I'm thirsty I can drink
Water at the river's brink:

When at night I go to sleep,
By my mother I must keep:
I am safe enough from cold
At her side within the fold."

AUTHOR UNKNOWN

THE LOST PUSSY

I'm lonesome for my pussy cat;
  She's been so long away;
Her dish of milk for breakfast
  Has not been touched today.
Here's Daddy splashing from the
  barn,
  Across the muddy ground;
His face has such a big smile,
  I think my kitty's found.
You'd never guess where Pussy is;
  She's hidden safe away,
With four black baby kittens;
  Their nest is in the hay.

LAURA E. THOMPSON

THE BARN

Within my doors the animals live
  That serve you every day—

The horse that plows the ground for
  you,
  And helps draw in the hay,

The gentle cows that give you milk,
  The cat that hunts for mice,

The dog that guards the sheep and
  the house—
  Oh! a barn's a place that's nice!

Within my doors there's friendliness,
  For no one quarrels here;

My friends are kindly treated
  Each day throughout the year.

M. LOUISE C. HASTINGS

MEDDLESOME MOUSE

One day a busy little mouse
Wanted to come into the house.
He didn't knock upon the door;
He gnawed a hole right in the floor;
And then he wandered all around.
He didn't hear a single sound.
There was some cheese upon a trap.
One nibble, and—the trap went
SNAP!

HELEN CARSON SHOEMAKE

THE COW

The friendly cow all red and white,
  I love with all my heart:
She gives me cream with all her
  might,
  To eat with apple-tart.

She wanders lowing here and there,
  And yet she cannot stray,
All in the pleasant open air,
  The pleasant light of day;

And blown by all the winds that pass
  And wet with all the showers,
She walks among the meadow grass
  And eats the meadow flowers.

ROBERT LOUIS STEVENSON

LITTLE DUCKLING'S BOAT

Little Duckling went out on the water
  so deep
And he sang as he swam with a lazy
  "Peep-peep."
Then at last he climbed up on his
  mother's broad back
While she swam all around with a
  sleepy "Quack-quack."
Said dear little Duckling, "You make
  a nice boat,
I like to ride this way while you swim
  and float."
Then she stopped her "Quack-quack,"
  and he stopped his "Peep-peep,"
And there on the water they floated
  asleep.

M. LUCILLE FORD

LEARNING TO TALK

The new little chicks say "Cheep,
  cheep, cheep!"
While the calf bawls sadly, "Maa!"
And the wee little frogs cry, "Peep,
  peep, peep!"
And the young crows croak, "Caa,
  caa!"

April's the time for learning to talk.
Just listen and you will hear!
The new little things that can hardly
  walk
Are speaking plain and clear.

But our little lazy baby boy
(He's six months old today.)
Can laugh and wave his arms for joy
But he hasn't a word to say!

INEZ GEORGE GRIDLEY

FAREWELL TO THE FARM

The coach is at the door at last;
The eager children, mounting fast
And kissing hands, in chorus sing:
Good-by, good-by, to everything!
To house and garden, field and lawn,
The meadow-gates we swung upon,
To pump and stable, tree and swing,
Good-by, good-by, to everything!

And fare you well for evermore,
O ladder at the hayloft door,
O hayloft where the cobwebs cling,
Good-by, good-by, to everything!
Crack goes the whip, and off we go;
The trees and houses smaller grow;
Last, round the woody turn we swing:
Good-by, good-by, to everything!

ROBERT LOUIS STEVENSON

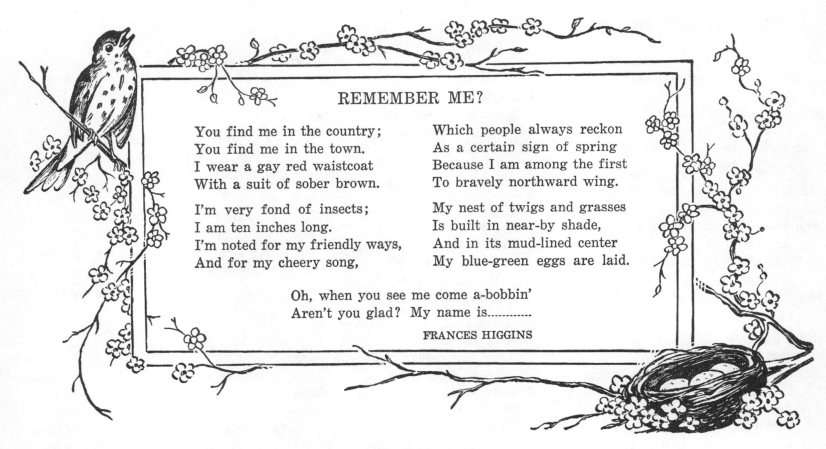

REMEMBER ME?

You find me in the country;
You find me in the town.
I wear a gay red waistcoat
With a suit of sober brown.

I'm very fond of insects;
I am ten inches long.
I'm noted for my friendly ways,
And for my cheery song,

Which people always reckon
As a certain sign of spring
Because I am among the first
To bravely northward wing.

My nest of twigs and grasses
Is built in near-by shade,
And in its mud-lined center
My blue-green eggs are laid.

Oh, when you see me come a-bobbin'
Aren't you glad? My name is............

FRANCES HIGGINS

THE BLUE JAY

A noisy blue jay in the tree
Outside my window screamed at me.
"Get up, get up," the blue jay said.
"Get up, get up, you sleepyhead!"

"All right," I said to the noisy jay.
"I'm getting up. Now go away."
"Get up," he screamed again and fled
To waken others still in bed.

RALPH MARCELLINO

FEED THE BIRDS

Don't forget the helpful birds
  When wintertime comes round!

Don't forget your feathered friends
  When snow and ice abound!

You have listened to their songs
  All the summer through.

Think of all the bugs and worms
  They have killed for you.

Now that they are hungry
  Tie suet in a tree;

Scatter crumbs and nuts about
  And see how glad they'll be.

LAURA M. CORYELL

TIME TO RISE

A birdie with a yellow bill
Hopped upon the window sill,
Cocked his shining eye and said:
"Ain't you 'shamed, you sleepyhead!"

ROBERT LOUIS STEVENSON

PIGEONS

I wish I could curl up coral toes
  And open pearl-blue wings,
And sail away on a shining day
  Over the top of things,

Till the world would look like a patch-
    work quilt
  Of fields and flower beds,
And the roads and the rivers would
    curl around
  Unravelling thin, like threads;

And a person would be the size of a
    doll,
  And a cow the size of a cat,
And a house would seem like a
    painted toy,
  As little and queer as that.

I'd tag a tower, and flick a wing
  Against a spire—and then
Come wild tobogganing down the
    wind,
  And flutter home again!

NANCY BYRD TURNER

CROWS

I wonder what crows talk about;
  They have so much to say.
Perhaps they're telling secrets
  In their own noisy way.
Perched on a tree or flying high
  In any kind of weather,
They harshly chatter fast and loud,
  Each time they get together.

EDDIE W. WILSON

BIRD MANNERS

Last night while we were all asleep
  A cloth of feathery snow
Was thickly spread upon the ground,
  And how the wind did blow!

We placed some breakfast for the
    birds
  Outside our kitchen door;
They gathered round the tablecloth—
  A hundred guests or more;

And as they ate they hopped about
  And chirped in friendly mood;
Then each one turned his tiny head
  And thanked us for the food.

GERTRUDE M. ROBINSON

THE RAGGEDY DOG

The raggedy dog is curly and brown;
He sits on the porch and looks up and
    down;
His eyes and his nose are little and
    black,
And he likes me to scratch his ears
    and his back.

When he sees a big dog he'll growl
    and he'll run,
And then he'll pretend he's only in
    fun,
And wag his short tail, and say, "How
    are you?"
In dog talk. That's just the best way
    to do.

But big dogs don't bother with those
    that are small;
They never notice the raggedy dog
    at all;
And he doesn't mind, for he knows
    that I care
For a little brown dog with raggedy
    hair.

                    BARBARA HANNA

MY CAT

When it rains
The birds put their raincoats on
    And under the leaves they hide;

But my kitten quite daintily
Walks through the grass
    To the house and steps inside!

                    M. LOUISE C. HASTINGS

SPORT

Sport walks along to school with me;
Sport is my dog; we're pals, you see.
He likes to race along and play,
And he's such company all the way;

But when we reach the schoolhouse
    lane,
I say, "Good-by. Run home to Jane."
Sometimes I give him bits of cake,
When he holds out his paw to shake.

When I come home from school at
    night,
Sport runs and barks with all his
    might,
And wags his tail to show his joy;
A dog's a good pal for a boy.

                    WINIFRED C. MARSHALL

KITTY CATS
AND BABY BATS

Two little kitty catkins
Met two little furry batkins
    Who folded up their thin, broad
        wings just so.
And the little kitty catkins
Whispered to the furry batkins,
    "Can you tell us where the catnip
        blossoms grow?"

    Said the cats, cats, cats,
    To the little furry bats,
        "Can you tell us?
        Oh, please tell us!"
    Said the cats, cats, cats.

Then the little furry batkins
Shouted to the kitty catkins,
    "Goodness gracious! Do you think
        that we are cats?"
"You have fur, sirs," said the catkins.
"Yes, and wings, too," said the bat-
    kins.
    "Oh!" said the catkins wisely,
        "You are bats!"

    "You are bats, bats, bats!"
    Cried the little kitty cats.
        "What an error!
        Such an error!
    You are bats, bats, bats!"

                    GUSSIE OSBORNE

KITTY PINKTONGUE

Friendly Kitty Pinktongue,
    White as morning milk,
Cuddles up to everyone,
    A bit of fluffy silk.

Playful Kitty Pinktongue
    Rolls like a ball of fur.
How she loves to chase her tail,
    And how she loves to purr!

Curious Kitty Pinktongue
    Hunts for something new,
Sniffs in corners, peeks in bins,
    And searches closets too.

Daring Kitty Pinktongue
    Learns to climb a stair,
Scampers to the very top,
    The attic—everywhere.

Tired Kitty Pinktongue,
    Asleep beside the fire,
Dreams of all the nicest things
    That little cats desire.

                    MAURICE HILL

OUR PETS

Jim's pet can bark and wag his tail,
    And do all kinds of tricks,
Like standing on his hind legs,
    And running after sticks;

While Polly's pet lives in a cage
    And sings 'most all day long.
Its pretty little yellow throat
    Keeps quivering with song.

My pet is soft and dressed in fur;
    She jumps up in my lap;
And when I stroke her silken coat,
    She purrs and takes a nap.

                    MABEL NIEDERMEYER

OUR PUPPY

We have the nicest puppy,
    And he belongs to me,
But Brother is so fond of him
    He owns him too, you see.

That puppy runs and races,
    And how he likes to play,
Around the yard and garden,
    'Most any time of day!

And when it's time for stories
    Almost as if he knew,
He cuddles down in Mother's lap
    And seems to listen too.

                    ALICE THORN FROST

FIVE LITTLE KITTY CATS

Five little kitty cats were sleeping
    on the floor,
One smelled a little mouse, then there
    were four.
Four little kitty cats came running
    after me,
A big dog ran and barked at them,
    and then there were three.
Three little kitty cats watched the
    birds who flew,
One went scampering up a tree, and
    then there were two.
Two little kitty cats were sleeping in
    the sun,
One jumped over the garden wall, and
    then there was one.
One lonely little kitty cat is looking
    for some fun,
He'll curl his tail and run away, and
    then there will be none!

                    FRANCES ARNOLD GREENWOOD

WISHES

I wish that animals could talk!
I'd love to hear the breathless tales
The tigers in a zoo could tell
Of shadowy, silent, jungle trails.

I'd like to listen to a seal,
And, oh! to have a kangaroo
Tell me what the girls and boys
Down in South Australia do!

I wonder, would the camels tell
All their memories of sand?
And just what would a Persian cat
Say about his native land?

But I'd be happy as I could be
If, the next time I go walking
With my spotted terrier, Rags,
Suddenly *he'd* start in talking!

ELAINE V. EMANS

ORGAN MONKEY

I am the organ monkey
You give your pennies to;
I always take my cap off
And make a bow to you.

I hope you like my jacket—
I like it anyway;
And see! I have a feather
In my cap today.

Our organ's old and shaky,
But its tunes sound good to me—
With "Little Annie Rooney"
And also "Sweet Marie."

ELSI PARRISH

TRESPASSERS

I saw a sign in Woodland Park
    That said, "Keep Off the Grass";
So I went slowly down the walk
    Where grown-up people pass.

I saw some robins on the lawn,
    And one prim meadow lark
Who preened his feathers in the sun
    As if he owned the park.

A fat green frog beside the pool
    Blinked lazily at me,
While ants and caterpillars crawled
    Beneath the maple tree.

Gray squirrels frolicked here and
    there;
    All creatures seemed so gay—
I hope no one who sees them there
    Will make them go away.

BLOSSOM BENNETT

KANGAROO RIDE

I suppose it would be rather
    A risky thing to do,
But I'd like to go out riding
    On a leaping kangaroo!

I expect it would be bumpy
    Each time he touched the ground,
And hard to keep from slipping,
    With every lengthy bound;

But I shouldn't mind the jolting,
    Or having people stare,
With Australian towns behind me,
    And cool wind in my hair!

ELAINE V. EMANS

AT THE ZOO

Bobby went to the zoo one day,
    To see all the animals there.
He saw a giraffe and a kangaroo,
    A gorilla and polar bear.
But he stayed and he stayed at the
        monkeys' cage
    As though he would never be
    through.
    They gamboled and pattered
    They clambered and clattered—
    The funniest things at the zoo.

He saw a yak, with its silky hair,
    Zebras and leopards and deer;
An armadillo all covered with scales,
    Which he thought was very queer.
But oh, the monkeys! the gay little
        monkeys
    With their merry hullabaloo!
    That frolicked and tumbled,
    And chattered and mumbled—
    The liveliest things at the zoo!

He saw a hippopotamus fat,
    Elephants vast in size,
Chamois, hyenas, tigers, and apes,
    And camels with scornful eyes.
But Bobby's heart was with none of
        these!
    What thrilled him through and
        through
    Were the queer little monkeys,
    The *dear* little monkeys,
    The monkeys he saw at the zoo!

LENA B. ELLINGWOOD

PETS

I'd like to have a puppy dog
    To romp and play with me—
Learn tricks and bark and wag his
        tail
    All day with eager glee.

I'd like to have a pony
    With a shaggy mane, to ride;
We'd canter, trot, and gallop
    Across the countryside.

I'd like to have a pussy cat
    With soft and silky fur;
I'd stroke her when she cuddled close
    And listen to her purr.

I'd like to have some bunnies
    With flapping ears so long,
And a wee canary bird
    To sing a merry song.

I'd like a turtle and a goat,
    A talking parrot, too—
If I had all the pets I want,
    Why, I could start a zoo!

LEONIE HUNTER

PENGUIN PARADE

I saw two little penguins walk
    Around the park's big lily pool.
I almost thought that they could talk;
    They marched as though they were
        in school!

With manner solemn and polite
    They bowed to everything they
        met;
Then waddled by—a funny sight—
    Their black-and-white suits shiny
    wet.

THEOBEL WING ALLEESON

IN THE PARK

I have a friend out in the park
Whose "hello" is just a bark;

He comes to meet me every day,
But always stays some feet away;

And every time that I come near,
He is quite sure to disappear;

He scampers up the nearest tree,
And then his tail is all I see.

How can I make him understand
I have some peanuts in my hand?

MABEL NIEDERMEYER

ADVENTURE

One night a little firefly
  Was looking at a star,
And said—but no one heard him—
  "I wonder what you are."
Then, eager for adventure,
  And brave as he could be,
He trimmed his little lantern
And flew away to see!

MAY JUSTUS

MY TOAD

Out in my little garden
  Lives a big hoptoad
Underneath the hollyhocks,
  Close to the road.

All day he is quiet,
  As still as can be;
Then in the night when it is dark
  He sings a song to me.

Although he has a squeaky voice,
  His song is very gay,
For he sings of the mosquitoes
  He has caught all day.

EVELINE NUTTER

AN EXPLANATION

I often think a butterfly
  With golden, shining wings
Most beautiful of all the earth's
  Wee flying things.

Sometimes I fancy that he is
  A sunbeam sailing 'round,
Flitting here and there so still
  He makes no sound.

And once I guessed how he is made:
  Upon his wings I saw
A diagram in black such as
  Someone might draw.

It looked as if whoever drew
  The lines had been in doubt,
And then was pleased, and so forgot
  To rub them out!

ARTHUR WALLACE PEACH

THE SWARM OF BEES

One little honeybee by my window
  flew;
Soon came another—then there were
  two.
Two happy honeybees in the apple
  tree;
One more bee came buzzing up—then
  there were three.
Three busy honeybees starting to
  explore
Another bee came to help—then there
  were four.
Four laden honeybees flying to the
  hive;
They were joined by one more bee—
  then there were five.
Five tired honeybees with the others
  mix;
Now there's a swarm of them—a
  hundred times six.

ELSA GORHAM BAKER

In Meadow Land

In Meadow Land, 'mid grasses green,
  There lives pert Mister Frog
Beside a little murm'ring stream,
  Beneath an old brown log.

In Meadow Land, down in soft earth,
  Lives Mister Turtle Black
Inside the yellow spotted shell
  He carries on his back.

I've heard it said, that in this land
  Resides queer Mrs. Mole,
A-keeping house the best she can
  'Way down a deep dark hole.

There're many folks in Meadow Land
  I know not much about;
But there's a big and busy crowd
  A-going in and out.

BUTTERFLIES

The little golden butterflies,
Like yellow pansies in disguise,
  Are tilting lightly on the blades
Of grass that sway in glad surprise.
They are such shining velvet things!
Each to a leaf or grass blade clings.
  Are they enchanted pansy maids?
Or did the fairies give them wings?

DORTHA KNAPP KILLIAN

EARTHWORM

Poor little earthworm
  Down in the ground,
Nobody loves you
  Or wants you around.

Often you're given
  To fishes as bait;
Often you're stepped on,
  When you're out too late.

But you, little earth worm,
  Keep working away,
Enriching and loosening
  The soil where you stay.

CLARA G. CORNELL

And Bumblebee and Butterfly
  And old Grasshopper Brown,
Will often visit there each day
  When on their way to town.

If you will go to Meadow Land
  Some day along with me,
I'm very sure you will be glad
  These meadow folks to see.

MYRA A. BUCK

LITTLE SQUIRREL

A little squirrel runs up and down
  In our old walnut tree.
All day he carries nuts away,
  As busy as can be.
Mother says he stores them safe
  For food when north winds blow;
I wonder how the squirrel knows
  That some day there'll be snow.

      ETHEL HOPPER

A WINTER INN

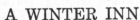

I know an inn that is safe and snug
  When wintry winds are blowing;
Its walls are thick, and its roof keeps
    out
  The cold when it is snowing.

The squirrels rent a little room
  When leaves blow helter-skelter,
And snowbirds wee come flocking
    there
  To share its welcome shelter.

The bright sun warms it through the
    day,
  And so it's never chilly,
Though breezes keen with icy breath
  Blow from the pastures chilly.

The spruces and the evergreens
  With needles thick and furry
Are inns to which, when cold winds
    blow,
  The wood-folk like to hurry!

      ARTHUR WALLACE PEACH

TIME TO PLAY

A rabbit said to Mr. Squirrel,
  One chilly autumn day,
"I think you are quite foolish
  To hide those nuts away."

"Oho! my friend," said Mr. Squirrel,
  "The cold winds soon will blow,
And nuts will all be hidden
  Deep under drifts of snow.

"Now that is why I'm working
  With all my strength to-day;
When winter comes, I'll doubtless
  Have time enough for play."

      ADA CLARK

SQUIRRELS

Some little red squirrels
Live up in a tree,
Out in the woodland gay.
They frisk and frolic,
And scamper about,
On each bright autumn day.

But they are not idle;
They're working away,
Busy as they can be,
Filling a storehouse,
For long winter days,
Thrifty and wise, you see.

      WINIFRED C. MARSHALL

THE "ROBBERS"

All the squirrels in the park
  Are tame as they can be,
And when I go there, afternoons,
  They come and play with me.

They peep into my luncheon box
  To see what they can find,
And though I call them "robbers,"
  I really do not mind.

The squirrels never tire of nuts,
  For breakfast, lunch, or tea,
They come and eat out of my hand,
  Then scamper up a tree.

      WINIFRED C. MARSHALL

BIRDS AND ANIMALS

HIBERNATING

The fat and sleepy woodchuck
And the brown and woolly bear
Have the nicest furry snow suits
That anyone could wear—

The very thing for sliding
Down a bank of frosty snow,
Or wearing on the skating rink
When winds of winter blow!

But those fat and lazy creatures
Wear their furry suits in bed;
No winter sports at all for them—
They hibernate instead.

Imagine fur pajamas!
What a funny thing to wear!
I'm glad I'm not a woodchuck
Or a big brown woolly bear!

INEZ GEORGE GRIDLEY

BUNNY TRACKS

Bunny tracks across the snow,
Crisscross, circles, there they go!
Up the hill in loping hop,
Bunny pauses when near the top
To sniff and snuff the frosty air,
For his mother said, "Take care!
Gleaming eyes are keen at night,
When the Moon Man's face is round
    and bright."

Bunny started home pell-mell,
When he heard old Screech Owl yell,
Down the hill in flying jumps,
Never minding humps and bumps,
Leaping, skipping, through the glen,
Under bushes, out again.
Crisscross, circles, there they go!
Bunny tracks across the snow.

ANN ROE ANDERSON

LITTLE BROWN BEAR

The little brown bear
    Is round as a tub.
We learned his name:
    They call him a cub.
He hides by his mother;
    He scratches his nose;
He won't catch the peanuts
    That anyone throws.
He leaves it to Daddy,
    Who likes to do that.
His daddy is big
    And shaggy and fat.
His mother is sleek,
    And, I think, very kind;
She plays with him roughly,
    But he doesn't mind.
The park is their home;
    I like to go there,
But I wish that *I* had
    A little brown bear.

IRMA DOVEY

The New Outfit

"I wish," said Willie Weasel, "that
I had a different coat and hat.
I'm awfully tired of wearing white;
I want a coat that's not so light."

"My gracious!" said his mother then,
"You'll get a nice brown outfit when
The new spring styles are on display,
But not upon this snowy day."

"I want it now. I hate to wait
Till such a long and far-off date."
So said wee William with a frown,
"It's brown I want; I want brown!"

Next morning when wee Willie woke,
His brothers thought it quite a joke
To find his wish had now come true;
A suit he had both brown and new!

Then Willie capered up and down,
And weasels eyed him, toe to crown.
What! Could springtime be so near?
It must be coming soon this year.

He scampered quickly to the wood,
Though Mother hadn't said he could.
"I'll show my friends a thing or two.
I'm sure they haven't suits so new!"

And then around the corner came
Old Slinky Coyote after game.
Poor Willie stood quite petrified
And hoped the snow would help him
    hide.

But his brown coat stood out so well
That Slinky spied him in the dell!
And then you should have seen them
    race
Back through the woods to Willie's
    place.

Poor Willie's heart thumped pitapat,
But Slinky stumbled and fell flat.
So Willie did get home all right;
Though suffering badly from the
    fright.

Now Willie must stay home awhile
Until brown suits are *ALL* in style.

AUDREY MCKIM

THE SQUIRREL

Whiskey, frisky,
Hippity hop,
Up he goes
To the tree top!
Whirly, twirly,
Round and round,
Down he scampers
To the ground.
Furly, curly
What a tail!
Tall as a feather
Broad as a sail!
Where's his supper?
In the shell.
Snappity, crackity,
Out it fell!

AUTHOR UNKNOWN

LITTLE BUNNY RABBITS

Oh, little bunny rabbits
    With funny little tails,
And ears so long you seem to me
    Like boats with furry sails,

You nibble at your cabbages;
    Your ears go flippy-flop.
Then all at once, you turn away,
    And hop and hop and hop!

FRANCES ARNOLD GREENWOOD

POEMS CHILDREN ENJOY

In Our Imagination

WISHES AND FISHES

Out in our garden
  Stands a little pool,
Where our goldfish swim
  In the sea grass cool.
One is silver,
  And one is gold,
And one is scarlet
  Like a dragon bold.

I sit on the edge,
  And oh, how I wish
For a lovely tail
  Like a bright goldfish.
And a sea-grass home,
  And nothing to do
But to swim and swim—
  You'd like it, too!

  JEAN PARMELEE

BOATS OF MELODY

At end of day, when lights are low,
In music boats we all may go
Across the seas to mystic lands
Of gay romance and fairy strands.

In music boats we sail and sway
To legend lands of far away;
We hear a dragon's mighty roar;
We moor our craft on History's shore.

The tender songs of long ago
Take us to lands we love and know,
While Mother-tunes, at twilight deep,
Can fill our eyes with dreams and
    sleep.

Oh, music is a precious thing;
Beautiful gifts its echoes bring,
Great gifts to those with eyes to see
The magic boats of melody.

SOLVEIG PAULSON RUSSELL

CINDERELLA POPCORN

Cinderella Popcorn's going to a ball,
To be held this evening in Corn
    Popper Hall,
Fairy Heat will change her dress
    from a tight, plain brown,
To a gorgeous, snowy white, ruffled
    all around.

Hopping, skipping, jumping, happy
    as a gnome,
Cinderella Popcorn's never going
    home,
See her, how she prances—will not
    stop at all,
Cinderella Popcorn, at the Popcorn
    Ball!

FRANCES GORMAN RISSER

SWING SONG

Perhaps I'll never really sail
    Across the ocean wide;
Perhaps I'll never touch the earth
    Upon the other side;
Perhaps I'll never climb the Alps
    Or ever see Peiping;
But I've a traveling game I play
    While swinging in my swing.

I go up high—so very high—
    And then I say to me,
"Now you are sailing far across
    A deep and rolling sea."
And when I've crossed the ocean
    blue,
    Why, then I just pretend
The sailing swing will carry me
    To London or Lands End.

So off I go to see the world,
    To see each splendid land:
The Blarney Stone in Ireland,
    The desert's golden sand,
A gondola in Venice,
    A bullfight in old Spain.
And then before we know it
    I'm swinging home again!

LELAND B. JACOBS

PRETENDING

I like to be a jumping jack
    And jump out from a box.
I like to be a rocking horse
    And rock and rock and rock.
I like to be a spinning top
    And spin around and round.
I like to be a rubber ball
    And bounce 'way up and down.

I like to be a big, fast train
    Whose wheels fly round and round.
I like to be a pony small
    And trot along the ground.
I like to be so many things—
    A growly, scowly bear—
But really I'm a little child
    Who sits upon a chair.

VIRGINIA LEE MALONEY

MUSIC

I sometimes wish that music
    Were something I could hold,
And carry all around with me
    In shining bands of gold.
I'd like to hold it in my hands
    And watch it throb and glow,
Or fade with shimmering loveliness
    In tempos sweet and slow.

But music is like summer winds,
    Or birds' wings, beating high,
Or fragrance from a flower,
    Or a baby's happy sigh.
We cannot bring it close enough
    To touch or really see,
So I am glad my ears can bring
    Its harmony to me.

SOLVEIG PAULSON RUSSELL

A JOLLY BATTLE

The pop-corn battle rages—
    Hear the bullets whizzing past!
The air is filled with popping guns,
    They're shooting thick and fast.

Each gallant pop-corn kernel,
    In snow-white uniform,
Is in the fight with all his might,
    And things are getting warm.

"Pop-pop!" you hear, and "pop-pop-
    pop!"
    Is answered without fail;
The clatter of the popping squads
    Is like a rain of hail.

A jolly pop-corn battle
    Is a most stirring sight;
But hard to tell, as you know well,
    Which side has won the fight.

And when the battle's over,
    The kernels, large and small,
From great to least will make a feast,
    And give a pop-corn ball.

MAUDE WOOD HENRY

POEMS CHILDREN ENJOY

WHITE HORSES

I see the clouds hurry over the hill,
Like frisky white horses that never
    stand still.
When I am a man and can climb very
    high,
Perhaps I can catch one galloping by.
I'll jump in the saddle, and, sitting
    astride,
With the wind for a whip, round the
    world I will ride.

ANNA M. PRIESTLEY

INDIAN VILLAGE

Grandfather's cornfield is covered o'er
With Indian wigwams, fifty or more;

There I play in a tepee brown,
A chieftain brave of this Indian
    town;

There I serve to bird and beast
Pumpkins and corn—a bounteous
    feast.

HILDRED TOPE

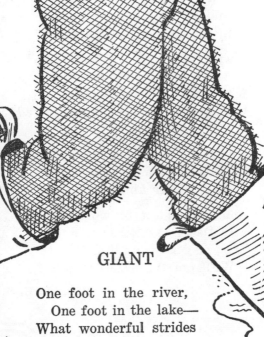

GIANT

One foot in the river,
    One foot in the lake—
What wonderful strides
    A giant can take!

The water goes "Squish"
    When he wiggles his toes.
Oh, giants have fun,
    As anyone knows.

His red rubber boots
    Reach up to his knee.
Why, puddles are nothing
    To giants like me!

ELIZABETH SAWYER

MY KITE

When I go out to fly my kite,
I hold the string so very tight
That it can't get away.

It sails away above the trees,
And talk with every passing breeze.
I wonder what they say.

They probably speak of foreign lands,
Of forests thick, and desert sands,
And many other things.

My kite has just a lot of fun,
While on the ground I have to run.
I wish that I had wings!

LEAH GIBBS KNOBBE

FAIRIES

Underneath the flowers,
Peeping through the grass,
Fairy folk are hiding
When grown-up people pass.

But if your eyes are open
As wide as they can be,
And you believe in fairies,
They're very plain to see.

LILLIAN MAE WEBB

MY DREAM

I dreamed I sat down on the sky
And cut out stars all day;
Then scattered them at purple dusk
To light the Milky Way.

I dreamed the Old Man Moon came up
And whispered in my ear:
"You'll have to clear away those stars
When morning dawns, my dear!"

ANNIE LEE FUNK

ON SUMMER DAYS

On summer days I'd like to be
    A walrus in a frozen sea;
I think it would be very nice
    To play "I spy" through holes of ice.

EDDIE W. WILSON

AN INDIAN CHIEFTAIN

I know a tall hill, grave and stately,
    Standing nobly in the sky,
Far above the vales and rivers,
    And the roads where men go by,

Like some bronzed chieftain gazing
    Over lands where long ago
Dwelt the people of his nation,
    Roaming freely to and fro.

The pines and spruces are a blanket
    Closely wrapped about his form,
Shielding him from wild winds,
    From the winter's chill and storm.

So I watch him and I fancy
    He is keeping guard until
His lost nation comes rejoicing
    Back to valley and to hill!

ARTHUR WALLACE PEACH

IN OUR IMAGINATION

WEE WINKY WIG

Wee fairy Winky Wig
Had never gone to school,
But when he'd grown to six moons
    old,
Because of fairy rule,
He had to take his little slate
Made from a tortoise shell,
And hurry to the fairy school
Down in the cowslip dell.

The teacher was a Bumblebee,
But very, very wise.
(Of course the dress of Bumblebee
Was just a gay disguise.)
And though she bumbled all about
She taught Wee Winky Wig
A lot of funny fairy facts
He'd need when he grew big.

Wee Winky Wig was very pleased
With all the things at school.
He liked to sit at his own desk
Made from a small toadstool;
He liked to read his fairy books
And dance and sing and run.
He said, "Why goodness gracious me!
School is so much fun!"

SOLVEIG PAULSON RUSSELL

MAGIC MOUSE

Wouldn't it be funny
    If a little magic mouse
Would eat up all the spinach
    In the garden and the house?

I wish, when Mother calls me
    And wants to wash my head.
A little mouse would whisper,
    "You may wash *my* head instead."

And when my toys are scattered
    Where I left them after play,
I'd love to have a magic mouse
    To put them all away.

And wouldn't it be wonderful
    If Dad and Mother said,
"You may stay up till midnight;
    We'll put the mouse to bed"?

EMILY H. HAX

FAIRY LORE

Deep in the heart of an Irish wood,
    Near a wishing well,
Wee folk are dancing in fairy rings
    To airy music's swell.

When the moon hangs low in the
        starlit sky,
    Shadowing the dell,
Hark! If you wish you can hear the
        sound
    Of a tinkling fairy bell.

Airy refrains can faintly be heard;
    Breezes rise and swell.
Whispering soft words, my bonny
        colleen,
    You're in a fairy dell!

MAXINE BELLEW

Peppermint Jane

In Lollipop Town, where the gum-
    drops grow,
Walked Peppermint Jane, down But-
    terscotch Row.

"Good day," said I with curtsy neat,
"You surely look good enough to eat,
    my sweet.

"You've a marshmallow hat with a
    taffy crown,
And lemon-drop beads on your choco-
    late gown,

"And a cinnamon mouth and a peanut
    nose,
And caramel shoes and peppermint
    hose!"

"Well, if you think I am sweet," said
    she,
"You may take just one small bite of
    me!"

So I took a bite of her taffy crown,
And another piece of her chocolate
    gown;

Her lemon beads and her peppermint
    hose
I ate and ate from her head to her
    toes.

"Stop, stop!" she cried with a licorice
    frown,
But I ate her up, till I ate her down.

And that was the end of Peppermint
    Jane,
In Lollipop Town, on Butterscotch
    Lane!   ELSIE M. FOWLER

POEMS CHILDREN ENJOY

Storybook Land

MAGIC KEYS

Oh, I am off to Storyland,
　　Where all the fairies dwell,
To watch them dance by moonlight
　　Down in a greenwood dell.

I'll next dine with a Highland chief,
　　In his great castle hall,
Or go with Cinderella
　　To the Fairy Prince's ball.

I'll follow wee quaint Alice
　　Down into Wonderland,
Then away to Sherwood Forest
　　With Robin's merry band.

I'll stroll with Robinson Crusoe,
　　Around his lonely isle,
Then fly to good King Arthur's court
　　And be a knight awhile.

Oh, I can sail the seven seas,
　　And fly o'er desert sand,
When I unlock with magic keys
　　The gates to Storyland.

CLARA RADER

WHO HATH A BOOK

Who hath a book
Has friends at hand,
And gold and gear
At his command;
And rich estates,
If he but look,
Are held by him
Who hath a book.

Who hath a book
Has but to read
And he may be
A king indeed;
His kingdom is
His inglenook;
All this is his
Who hath a book.

WILBUR D. NESBIT

I LIKE A BOOK

I like a book. It tells me things
Of ancient peoples and their kings
And what they used to do;
Of giants in some far-off land
And things I hardly understand,
Both make-believe and true.

I like books. It's fun to see
How interesting they can be—
As people are. And so
I try to treat them like a friend
And many pleasant hours spend
In learning what they know.

M. LUCILLE FORD

BOOK TRAVELS

Have you ever gone a-traveling
    On a very rainy day?
With a book and cozy corner
    Is the very nicest way.

Yesterday I went to Holland
    Where the tulip gardens grow,
And the people look so funny
    With their wooden shoes, you know.

Then, one day I went to Venice,
    Such a queer Italian town,
Where the streets are all of water,
    And the boats sail up and down.

Have you ever been to Scotland,
    Out among the heather bloom?
Just last week, the Scotch in kilties
    Came to see me in this room.

Oh, there are so many places—
    England, Italy, France and Spain;
Come and go a-traveling with me,
    When I visit them again.

GERTRUDE M. ROBINSON

THE LAND OF STORY BOOKS

At evening, when the lamp is lit,
Around the fire my parents sit;
They sit at home and talk and sing,
And do not play at anything.

Now, with my little gun, I crawl
All in the dark along the wall,
And follow round the forest track
Away behind the sofa back.

There in the night, where none can
    spy,
All in my hunter's camp I lie,
And play at books that I have read
Till it is time to go to bed.

These are the hills, these are the
    woods,
These are my starry solitudes;
And there the river on whose brink
The roaring lions come to drink.

I see the others far away
As if in firelit camp they lay
And I, like to an Indian scout,
Around their party prowled about.

So, when my nurse comes in for me,
Home I return across the sea
And go to bed with backward looks
At my dear land of Story Books.

ROBERT LOUIS STEVENSON

MY STORYBOOK

While Puss curls at my feet to dream
Of fat, fat mice and bowls of cream,
I like to sit for hours and look
Through my favorite storybook.

I read about the strangest things:
Wild animals that talk, and kings,
Lost princesses, and hidden gold,
And birds, and elves, and pirates bold.

There's nothing I like more to do;
And though 'tis sad, yet it is true,
It seems to me I've never read
Enough when I must go to bed!

ELAINE V. EMANS

LIBRARY CORNER

Have you seen my little harbor,
    My quaint little harbor,
        My magical harbor of dreams?
It's nothing but a corner,
    A library corner,
        Where books bring my cargo
        downstream.

And to this quaint corner
    Come Little Jack Horner,
        Tiny Tim, Crusoe, and Huck;
Come pirates with treasures,
    And jesters with pleasures,
        Like one-legged John Silver and
        Puck.

Whenever I'm weary,
    When evenings are dreary,
        I anchor in my little port;
I open a book,
    In my magical nook,
        And I'm bound to meet friends of
        some sort.

Not one e'er will leave me,
    Not one will deceive me,
        With a smile, each bright face
        always gleams.
We're comrades forever,
    For they wait for me, ever,
        In my library corner-of-dreams.

BERNARD HIRSHBERG

POEMS CHILDREN ENJOY

PICTURE BOOKS

I can skip skips
   With my red skipping rope.
I can blow bubbles
   With soap-bubble soap.

I can roll hoops
   And hippety-hop.
I can spin tunes
   With my musical top.

I can go sliding
   And merry-go-rounding
And bounce my big ball
   To the end of the counting.

But nothing is half
   So delightful to me
As looking at picture books
   Just before tea.

      J. VAN DOLZEN PEASE

BOOKS

Books are friends who take you far
   Wherever you would go,
From torrid lands and jungle ways
   To northern fields of snow.

Books bring us gifts from long ago
   And hints of future days,
And lead the mind refreshingly
   On unfamiliar ways.

Books are the chests of pirate gold
   Where wealth in stories lies
As varied as the clouds that blow
   Across November skies.

      SOLVEIG PAULSON RUSSELL

I COOK

I have a book of recipes
   To tell me how to cook.
On Saturdays I sometimes think
   It is my favorite book.

One morning I cooked breakfast:
   The bacon, eggs, and toast,
And Daddy said, "Hooray! Hooray!
   You're my favorite cook—almost."

I didn't mind the "almost,"
   For that just means that Mother
Is the cook that Dad and I
   Like more than any other.

      LUCRETIA PENNY

MY BOOKS

Through books I learn to really know
Just how the trees and blossoms grow,
And how the children far away
All dance and sing and work and play
    The livelong day.

The tales of fairies, goblins, elves,
That stand in rows upon my shelves,
Set all my fancies dancing free,
As my dear mother reads to me
    Of elfin glee!

Around the world I journey far;
I know the song of sea and star.
I read of kings and knights of old,
Of field and forest, wealth and gold,
    And warriors bold.

Oh! Won't you all now join the band
That finds true joy in Story Land,
For knowledge is a magic key
That opens doors for you and me
    So easily!

      ETHEL HAWTHORNE TEWKSBURY

READING BOOKS

I like to read all kinds of books
To entertain myself,
And so I'm glad when I can take
A book down from the shelf.

I like the picture books of planes,
Of flowers, birds, and ships
From which I can imagine that
I'm taking wonder trips.

I like the books with stories in
And also books of rhymes;
I often try to learn a few
And say them lots of times.

I like to read *all* kinds of books
I find upon the shelf—
Particularly now that I
Can read all by myself!

      VIVIAN G. GOULED

AN ADVENTURER

I relive each deed
Whenever I read
Of the past ages
In my history pages!

I cross desert sands
And visit strange lands;
I explore every sea
In geography!

And I am a knight
Wearing armor bright,
Whenever I look
In my storybook!

      ELAINE V. EMANS

SHOPPING

I like to hop, and I like to skip,
And I like to go on a shopping trip.

I like to stand by the bookman's shelf
And choose a book all by myself!

      J. VAN DOLZEN PEASE

MY GARDEN

I'm planting a garden out of a book.
   It tells the most wonderful things:
How to spade up the ground and rake
   quite fine,
   How to straighten the rows with
   long strings,
How to fasten tomatoes up to a stake,
   How to shield tender plants from
   the sun,

How to put in beans with the "eye
   side" down—
   Oh, a garden will be such fun!
My book describes slugs and aphids
   and worms,
   It tells about purchasing seeds;
But one thing is lacking: the book
   does not say
   How to tell the plants from the
   weeds!

      LAURA ALICE BOYD

THE LAND OF BOOKS

There's a wonderful land that I visit
    each day
Where pleasure trips beckon me free-
    ly to stray
'Midst wide, sunny hillsides, or still,
    hidden glens,
To mountains and seasides, to mead-
    ows and fens,
And far foreign landscapes in splen-
    did array.

In this wonderful land where I visit
    I see
Such interesting people all calling to
    me;
Fine soldiers, gay princes, and pirates
    so bold,
And planters, and craftsmen, and
    seekers for gold—
A clever and rollicking company.

To go to this land with its islands and
    brooks,
Its cowboys, detectives, and cannibal
    cooks,
No ticket you buy. For the asking it's
    free.
Just the cover you turn and adventur-
    ing you'll be
In this wonderful, magical kingdom
    of books.

              LELAND B. JACOBS

BORROWING A BOOK

When someone lends a book to me,
I handle it most carefully.
I keep the pages flat and clean,

And never put things in between;
And just as soon as I am through
I give it back, and say, "Thank you!"

              VIVIAN G. GOULED

MAGIC KEYS

Would you like to travel far
From the place where now you are?
    Read a book.

Would you nature's secrets know,
How her children live and grow?
    Read a book.

Is it adventure that you crave,
On land or on ocean wave?
    Read a book.

Would you like to talk with kings?
Or to fly with Lindbergh's wings?
    Read a book.

Would you look on days gone by?
Know scientific reasons why?
    Read a book.

The world before you will unfold,
For a magic key you hold
    In a book.

             LEAH GIBBS KNOBBE

THE DICTIONARY

I hope that I shall never be
Devoid of curiosity
About the meaning of a word
Which I have either seen or heard.

I hope when of a word I'm wary,
I'll always seek a dictionary,
And learn to use it as a friend
For help and counsel without end.

             GENIEVE P. BRUNKOW

GOING TO THE LIBRARY

I walk inside a building where
    The children's room I see,
With pretty books all round about—
    They're waiting there for me.

Gay flowers are painted on the walls,
    And story folks I know,
Who live inside the books I read—
    All round the room they go.

I take my book, and then I find
    A table with a chair.
I want to read about a knight
    Who saves his lady fair.

I'm in a pirate ship at sea;
    I'm hunting buffalo.
Oh, anywhere I open books,
    Adventuring I go.

          ELLA WATERBURY GARDNER

MY BOOKS

I have a little bookshelf,
And on it, in a row,
Are all the nicest storybooks
A child could ever know.

And if you'll come to see me,
As I shall hope you do,
I'll bring my finest storybooks
And read them all to you.

            MAUDE M. GRANT

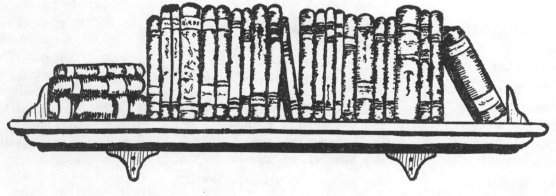

In the Long Ago

LONG, LONG AGO

Did you ever stop to think
That long, long ago,
There were no motor cars
Passing in a row!

There were no trains
On long, shining tracks,
No mighty steamboats
With tall smokestacks!

No mail man stopping
At every door,
No truck with packages
Bought at the store!

Who were the bearers
Of burdens then?
The sturdy backs
Of brave, strong men!

J. VAN DOLZEN PEASE

COLONIAL DAYS

A very young miss
  In George Washington's day
Would go out to ride
  With a horse and a sleigh.
She would wear a long cloak
  And a hood lined with down
And buckled shoes twinkling
  From under her gown.

KATE ENGLEHARDT CLARK

HOW WASHINGTON DRESSED

When Washington was president,
  He wore the queerest clothes;
His shoes had silver buckles on—
  Now, why, do you suppose?

His suit was made of velvet cloth
  With buckles at the knee;
He wore lace ruffles on his coat
  When he went out to tea.

His hair was tied with ribbons, too,
  And braided like a girl's.
How could he be a president,
  And wear his hair in curls?

GERTRUDE M. ROBINSON

THE COVERED WAGON

When our forefathers
With courage true
Left the old home
For the new,

'Neath starry sky
And blazing sun
The covered wagon
Was their home.

Sheltering them
By night and day,
Bearing them safely
On their way,

Carrying in
Its circling fold
The homely comforts
Loved of old,

Faithful
Till the journey's end,
The covered wagon
Was their friend.

J. VAN DOLZEN PEASE

THERE WAS A LITTLE GIRL

There was a little girl, who had a
    little curl
  Right in the middle of her fore-
    head,
And when she was good, she was
    very, very good,
  But when she was bad she was
    horrid.

She stood on her head, on her little
    trundle-bed,
  With nobody by for to hinder;
She screamed and she squalled, she
    yelled and she bawled,
And drummed her little heels against
    the winder.

Her mother heard the noise, and
    thought it was the boys
  Playing in the attic,
She rushed upstairs, and caught her
    unawares,
  And spanked her, most emphatic.

AUTHOR UNKNOWN

THE STAGECOACH

Down the valley and over the hill,
With whirling wheels and hoofbeats
    drumming,
Near and nearer and nearer still,
The stagecoach is coming! The stage-
    coach is coming!

High on his seat see the driver ride!
He cracks his whip and calls aloud.
The people run from every side,
A welcoming and joyful crowd.

Bag and baggage piled on high
Sway against the setting sun!
Like clouds across the wind-blown
    sky,
The dashing horses onward run!

With beating hearts and happy
    smiles,
Proudly the travelers sit within,
How wonderfully swift the journey-
    ing miles!
How wondrously sweet the welcoming
    din!

Down the valley and over the hill,
With whirling wheels and hoofbeats
    drumming,
Near and nearer and nearer still,
The stagecoach is coming! The stage-
    coach is coming!

JOSEPHINE VAN DOLZEN PEASE

SONG OF LONG-AGO CHILDREN

The long-ago children—
  What did they know,
With no telephones,
  And no radio?

Without our autos
  And airplanes fast,
How did ever
  The time go past?

What would they think
  Of poles and wires,
And voices round
  The winter fires,

Talking to them
  From everywhere?
These would surely
  Give them a scare,

Until they knew
  About it all—
Marconi, and the
  Long-distance call.

NORMAN C. SCHLICHTER

THE LAMPLIGHTER

My tea is nearly ready and the sun
  has left the sky;
It's time to take the window to see
  Leerie going by;
For every night at teatime and before
  you take your seat,
With lantern and with ladder he
  comes posting up the street.

Now Tom would be a driver and
  Maria go to sea,
And my papa's a banker and as rich
  as he can be;
But I, when I am stronger and can
  choose what I'm to do,
O Leerie, I'll go round at night and
  light the lamps with you!

For we are very lucky, with a lamp
  before the door,
And Leerie stops to light it as he
  lights so many more:
And O! before you hurry by with
  ladder and with light;
O Leerie, see a little child and nod to
  him tonight!

ROBERT LOUIS STEVENSON

The Dorchester Giant

There was a giant in times of old,
  A mighty one was he;
He had a wife, but she was a scold,
So he kept her shut in his mammoth
    fold;
  And he had children three.

It happened to be an election day,
  And the giants were choosing a
    king;
The people were not democrats then,
They did not talk of the rights of
    men,
  And all that sort of thing.

Then the giant took his children
    three,
  And fastened them in the pen;
The children roared; quoth the giant,
    "Be still!"
And Dorchester Heights and Milton
    Hill
  Rolled back the sound again.

Then he brought them a pudding
    stuffed with plums,
  As big as the State House dome;

Quoth he, "There's something for you
    to eat;
So stop your mouths with your
    'lection treat,
  And wait till your dad comes
    home."

So the giant pulled him a chestnut
    stout,
  And whittled the boughs away;
The boys and their mother set up a
    shout,
Said he, "You're in and you can't
    get out,
  Bellow as loud as you may."

Off he went and he growled a tune
  As he strode the fields along;
'Tis said a buffalo fainted away,
And fell as cold as a lump of clay,
  When he heard the giant's song.

But whether the story's true or not,
  It isn't for me to show;
There's many a thing that's twice as
    queer
In somebody's lectures that we hear,
  And those are true you know.

What are those lone ones doing now,
  The wife and the children sad?
Oh, they are in a terrible rout,
Screaming, and throwing their pud-
    ding about,
  Acting as if they were mad.

They flung it over to Roxbury hills,
  They flung it over the plain,
And all over Milton and Dorchester
    too
Great lumps of pudding the giants
    threw;
  They tumbled as thick as rain.

Giant and mammoth have passed
    away,
  For ages have floated by;
The suet is hard as a marrowbone,
And every plum is turned to a stone,
  But there the puddings lie.

And if, some pleasant afternoon,
  You'll ask me out to ride,
The whole of the story I will tell,
You shall see where the puddings fell,
  And pay for the punch beside.

OLIVER WENDELL HOLMES

THE BUTTON BOX

My grandmother's button box
Is a delight to see;
There are all sorts of buttons,
Each with a history.

There are the tiny buttons
That held Dad's clothes in place
When he was a little tad
Who liked to romp and race.

And then there are the buttons
Granddaddy wore on gray,
When he stood by Grandmother
Upon their wedding day.

There are dainty pearl buttons
That Mother used to wear,
When she was seventeen,
So pretty, young, and fair.

There are big wooden buttons
From great-grandfather's suit
And fancy brass ones he wore,
When he played the flute.

I love that old button box
When Grandmother sits with me,
And picks out all the buttons
With a family history!

HELEN KITCHELL EVANS

MEHITABLE

Great-Grandmother's doll, Mehitable,
    In her quaint old-fashioned gown,
Is dressed exactly the way she was
    When she came from London town.
She wears a bonnet and cloak of gray,
    And looks like a Quaker maid;
She thinks the dolls in their Paris
        gowns
    Quite worldly, I am afraid.

I always feel that she's very wise—
    She has lived so long, you see.
If she could speak, I am very sure,
    She would tell strange tales to me.
I take great care of Mehitable,
    In her quaint old-fashioned gown,
Great-Grandmother's doll of long ago,
    Whose home was in Boston town.

WINIFRED C. MARSHALL

FRANKLIN'S KITE

When Franklin flew his famous kite
    And drew the lightning's fire,
Coaxing from thunder-clouds the
        bright
    Sparks on his "pointed wire,"
I wonder if he visioned how
    Electricity
Would be the servant it is now
    Of domesticity!

Ben Franklin could not "plug it in"
    And get his coffee boiling;
Nor start the toaster with a grin,
    Then go back to his toiling;
Good Madame Franklin did not use
    The "current" for her cleaning;
Nor dreamed that "Monday Wash
        Day Blues"
    Ben's "find" would rob of meaning!

Wherefore, as we turn on the light
    Which sends the shadows fleeting,
Or press a button when at night
    We feel it's time for eating,
Let's honor early scientist Ben,—
    His kite amid the thunder—
Since, but for pioneering then,
    Would there be an age of wonder?

CLARENCE MANSFIELD LINDSAY

When Grandma Went To School

My grandma often tells me tales
    Of days long, long ago,
And how they used to knit and spin,
    And every girl could sew.
But how I love to cuddle close
    On her old worn footstool
And listen to her tell again
    Of when she went to school.

The schoolhouse then was made of logs,
    And all the benches, too;
Without a back to lean against—
    I wonder what I'd do?
But they just had to sit up straight,
    And mind the teacher's rule,
Or else they wore a big dunce cap,
    When Grandma went to school.

They all used slates and pencils, too,
    Or else a goose-quill pen,
For buying tablets every week
    Was never heard of then.
And when I talk of lunches, hot,
    She says with ridicule:
"We used to have to eat 'em cold,
    When I was sent to school."

She talks about the old "Three R's,"
    And how she learned them well,
She was sure when she was young,
    Children were taught to spell.
They had to mind and study, too,
    And had no time to fool.
It couldn't really have been fun
    When Grandma went to school.

EFFIE CRAWFORD

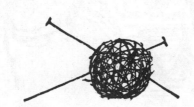

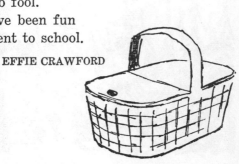

The World Around Us

BALLS

The moon, it is a silver ball.
  The sun's a ball of gold.
In wintertime the icy hail
  Forms balls, so small and cold.

Green vines in summer bear gay balls
  Of berries, as they climb;
And mistletoe and holly balls
  Greet us at Christmas time.

The orchard trees hang full of balls—
  Red cherries, apples round;
And in the field great pumpkin balls
  In autumn can be found.

They're everywhere—on earth, in
    sky—
  And really, after all,
The earth itself, so big and fair,
  Is just another ball!

FRANCES GORMAN RISSER

MORNING TOAST

My toast has such a nice crunchable
    sound
As I bite my piece that's all buttered
    and browned.
Though my egg is pure silver and
    gold in my dish,
And my orange and cocoa quite all
    one could wish
Still, I know that at breakfast the
    thing I like most
Is my buttered, brown, munchable,
    crunchable toast!

DORIS I. BATEMAN

TAFFY MAKING

First you light the fire and
    Get the kettle out.
Then all the pleasant kitchen tasks
    Are turn and turn about.

One measures out the sugar
    And the butter that goes in it.
Another tries the syrup
    And counts each boiling minute.

You fetch the biggest platter
    And make sure it's greased all
    right;
Then all scrub hands again and
    wait—
    It's taffy-making night!

REVAH SUMMERSGILL

DRINKING MILK

Milk is very good to drink;
    It is so pure and white.
It makes our teeth grow healthily
    And our bones grow right
Milk is such a pleasant drink;
    It tastes so fresh and sweet.
We should always have a glass
    Every time we eat.

SOLVEIG PAULSON RUSSELL

THE FRIENDLY DARK

The friendly dark just fills my room
    When I'm in bed at night;

It creeps on tiptoe all around
    To take the place of light.

BARBARA HANNA

PLAY OCEAN

The foam-flecked waves dash all
    about!
    The ocean's deep and blue!
I'm not afraid—I duck my head,
    And swim a mile or two!

I splash and float, don't need a boat,
    For my blue sea's the tub!
'Midst soapsuds foam I paddle
    home—
    And scrub and scrub
    And SCRUB!

FRANCES GORMAN RISSER

THE COOKYMAN

Mother baked a cooky man
In a pan for me,
With nuts for buttons down his coat,
And raisin eyes to see.
His mouth is made of cherry bits
Curved in a smile so sweet;
I think I'll have to save him, for
He's much too nice to eat.

LEONIE HUNTER

MY PENNY PIG

I have a roly-poly pig
    That stands upon a shelf,
And gobbles up my copper cents
    Each day, to feed himself!

He'd never take a beauty prize,
    He's homely as can be,
But my fat "penny pig" is worth
    His weight in cents to me!

FRANCES GORMAN RISSER

I WOULDN'T MISS IT

I'm always in the kitchen
When Mother's there to bake,
Because I like to watch her
Spread frosting on a cake.

She does it very quickly—
It hardly takes a minute—
And then she lets me lick the bowl
That had the frosting in it!

LUCRETIA PENNY

AN INFORMATION BUREAU

An information bureau right in our
    home you'll find.
Of course it is our mother, so loving
    and so kind.
For she's the one we go to; a question
    each one brings.
We're sure that she can tell us just
    where we left our things.

"Where is my hat?" That's Father;
    and Jack's mislaid a book.
"I've lost my specs," calls Grandma.
    "Please, will you give a look?"
"Where is my scarf?" asks Sister. "I
    left it in the hall."
And Dave comes in demanding,
    "Where's that new tennis ball?"

"Where are my gloves?" says Grand-
    pa. "I need them right away."
"I've lost my notebook, Mother. I had
    it yesterday."
An information bureau, yes, really
    that is so;
We always go to Mother, and Mother
    seems to know.

BLANCHE SPRAGUE

GRANDPA'S CLOCK

"Now, go to bed,"
Says Grandpa's clock.
"Tick-tock, tick-tock,
Tick-tock, tick-tock!"
So I put down my big red block,
And then pull off each wrinkled sock.

ALICE F. GREEN

WHO KNOWS?

Clocks know two words: "Tick, tock!"
  My watch knows one word:
    "Tick!"
I wish my little watch would learn
  The big clocks' clever trick;

But watches look like baby clocks,
  And if my small watch grows,
It may add "Tock!" on to its "Tick!"
  Perhaps it will! Who knows?

FRANCES GORMAN RISSER

IT'S BEDTIME THEN

A good clock never hurries,
  A good clock's never slow;
And so when ours says "Bedtime,"
  It's *bedtime* then, I know.

I can't ask our clock to wait—
  Good clocks don't wait, you see—
So when our clock says "Bedtime,"
  It's *bedtime* then for me.

LUCRETIA PENNY

THE CUCKOO CLOCK

Grandma has a cuckoo clock.
  It looks just like a house.
I often sit and watch it,
  As quiet as a mouse.
When the small door opens,
  The cuckoo bows to me,
Looks at the time upon the clock,
  And sings out cheerily,
  "Cuckoo, cuckoo, cuckoo!"

LEONIE HUNTER

LEARNING TO TELEPHONE

"Ding-a-ling! Ding-a-ling-ling!"
  That's the way it rings.
I answer it for Mother—
  And once I ordered things.

She said, "Please call the grocer,
  And say, 'One pound of tea,
Three lemons and three oranges,
  And kindly send to me.'"

I said it very clearly,
  As Mother said I should.
When I was done she smiled at me,
  And said, "I knew you could."

So now I know she'll let me
  Telephone again,
For things to other people
  Besides the groceryman.

NORMAN C. SCHLICHTER

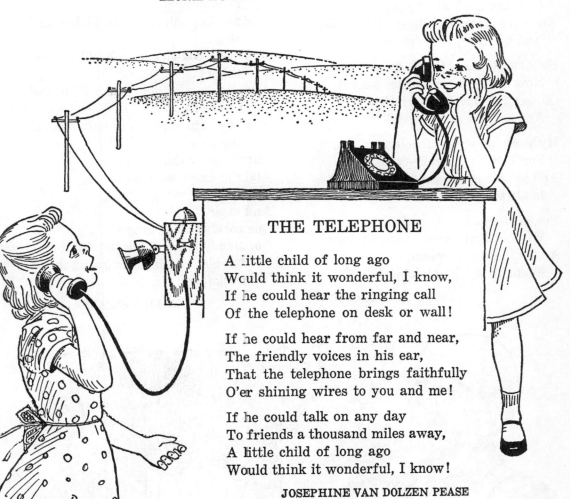

THE TELEPHONE

A little child of long ago
Would think it wonderful, I know,
If he could hear the ringing call
Of the telephone on desk or wall!

If he could hear from far and near,
The friendly voices in his ear,
That the telephone brings faithfully
O'er shining wires to you and me!

If he could talk on any day
To friends a thousand miles away,
A little child of long ago
Would think it wonderful, I know!

JOSEPHINE VAN DOLZEN PEASE

THE WORLD AROUND US

GRANDMA'S COOKY JAR

My grandma has a cooky jar
Up high upon a shelf,
And when I go to visit her,
She says, "Just help yourself."
So then I climb upon a chair
And reach up very tall,
And put my hand 'way down inside—
I'm careful not to fall.

Sometimes I find they're round and
    sweet;
Sometimes they're filled with spice;
And then again all sorts of shapes;
But any kind is nice.
When Grandma hears I'm coming
    soon,
She starts right in to bake,
And knows that I shall always like
Whatever kind she'll make.

BARBARA HANNA

GRANDPA'S GARDEN

My grandpa has a garden
  That never wilts or fades,
Although he never plows it up,
  Or waters it, or spades.

He never worries if it storms,
  Or fears the hottest sun;
And yet his garden's filled with plants,
  And he just loves each one!

He'll say to me, "Come, take a look.
  Now aren't those pansies sweet!
Oh, see this lovely hyacinth—
  And here's a marguerite!"

My grandpa's very feeble,
  For he's past eighty-nine
And yet his lovely garden
  Is always in its prime:

Yes, Grandpa has a garden
  Without scarecrow, fence, or dog;
And, all in lovely colors,
  Keeps it in his catalogue!

SARAH GRAMES CLARK

CANDLE MAKING

Dip the wick into the tallow,
Melted hot and golden yellow.
Watch it grow,
Watch it grow,
Like a rolling ball of snow.

In and out and in again,
Dip and dip and dip, and then,
Round and smooth
And candle-thick,
Put it in the candlestick.

  Through the darkness
  Of the night,
  It will make
  A lovely light.

J. VAN DOLZEN PEASE

THE OLD ROCKING CHAIR

At teatime I climb on my dear daddy's
  knee
In the old rocking chair, and he rocks
  with me;
We laugh at the wind, when it roars
  loud outside,
So cozy are we on our rocking-chair
  ride.
And Mother will rattle the dishes, and
  sing;
And the wood fire crackles like ev'ry-
  thing!
And the puppy dog thumps his tail
  on the floor;
And the rain spatters crossly against
  the door.
But the more the rain falls,
And the more the wind blows,
The snugger
And nicer
Our rocking chair grows!
Oh, Daddy and I think it jolly to be
In the old rocking chair, when he
  rocks with me.

MARIAN STEARNS CURRY

THE BLUE TEAPOT

This little blue teapot,
With figures of gold,
Belonged to Grandmother,
So I have been told;
And since I have her name,
Which is Sue Adeline,
The little blue teapot
Will one day be mine.

They tell me Grandmother
Was gentle and fair,
With laughing blue eyes
And soft curly hair.
Though I never saw her,
I play, as you see,
That I am Grandmother,
When I'm pouring tea.

WINIFRED C. MARSHALL

THE PONY

'Way up among the maple boughs
  Against the bending sky,
With nimble hoofs and plumy tail,
  A pony prances high.
I'd like to ride that pony gay,
  And when the breezes blew
To race the birds and flying clouds;
  That's what I'd like to do.
What fun to smooth his shining head
  And proud uplifted mane!
But he's on top of Grandpa's barn,
  A jolly weather vane.

ALICE THORN FROST

SOMEONE I KNOW

He never has a thing to say,
  But in one place he stays
Through sun and shine, through wind
  and rain,
  No matter what the days.
He is useful where he stands,
  Although he says no word;
He merely points—we understand
  As if real talk we heard.

He makes me think of folks I know
  Who never wander far,
But who, through kindly ways and
  deeds,
  To us of service are.
That he can help me, I know well,
  Since I have ample proof;
I see him now—the weather-vane
Upon my neighbor's roof!

ARTHUR WALLACE PEACH

Auntie's House

I like to visit Auntie's house.
   She makes the best desserts—
Marshmallow puddings and tarts.
   Cookies, shaped like rings and
      hearts.

First, when I went there, I would say:
   "I don't like this or that;
No spinach for me, Auntie, dear,
   Oh, my! carrots taste so queer!"

Then Auntie said that at her house
   There never was dessert
For anyone not eating nice
   Fresh vegetables, prunes, and rice.

So, there was nothing else to do
   But eat just all she served.
And oh! a joke on me, I'll tell:
   I really like them now quite well.

HELEN C. SHOEMAKE

THEY COME IN PAIRS

So many objects
Are purchased by twos:
Gloves and house slippers
And cymbals and shoes;
Galoshes and ear muffs
And ice skates and skis;
Roller skates, stockings,
And still more of these;
Curtains; and earrings
For ladies; and then,
Trousers and socks
And cuff links for men.
It seems to me
There are pairs by the score.
Do you think that you
Could suggest any more?

VIVIAN G. GOULED

A LUMP OF CLAY

I took a little gray lump of clay
And rolled it into a ball today.

I pinched it there and I pinched it
   here.
I pulled out a trunk and a floppy ear;

Another ear on the other side,
Four gray legs that were sturdy and
   wide,

A thinny-thin tail where a tail should
   be—
And there stood an elephant looking
   at me!

IRENE U. HARTWELL

TRY IT SOMETIME

I like music, mudpies, and mush,
And ribbons and roses and wrens.
I like cookies and cats and kites
And hopscotch and horses and hens.
It's fun to make an "I like" list—
To watch it grow and grow and grow.
I like picnics and pups and pinks
And sandpiles and sunshine and
   snow.

M. LUCILLE FORD

WORDS

Words are the oddest things
   Haven't you found?
Sometimes they don't look a
   Bit like they sound.

There are "to," "too," and "two."
   Watch which you're using!
If you're not a good speller, it's
   Very confusing.

Sometimes one word can mean
   Different things;
We draw with straight "rulers"
   Or else it means "kings."

Then you recite "bow,"
   But shoot with a "bow."
Words are the oddest things!
   Don't you think so?

NELLE ARNOLD

THE RAINDROP SONG

The raindrops on the roof at night
   Are like a lullaby.
I cannot keep my eyelids up,
   No matter how I try.

Their pitter-patter, soft and low,
   Makes such a pleasant song;
I'd like to lie awake and hear
   Their notes the whole night long.

But slowly, slowly, sleep steals on—
   I want to listen so!
The Sandman's winning once again—
   To Slumberland I go.

MOLLIE B. HERMAN

SOUNDS

I like the sound of many things—
Of tinkling streams, a bird that sings,
Of falling raindrops, buzzing bees,
Of crunching snow, and wind in trees.

I like the sound of happy play,
Of echoes soft and far away,
Of music gay or sweet and slow,
Of trains and cars that swiftly go.

But there is one sound nicer far
To me than all these others are;
I like the sound September brings
When once again the school bell rings.

M. LUCILLE FORD

ERRANDS

Roller skating, roller skating,
    On errands I can go
With a clatter, clatter, clatter,
    More often fast than slow.
Doing errands for the folks,
    While skating, makes it fun;
It's like playing while you work—
    A sort of two in one.

IVA RIEBEL JUDY

MY KITE

I have a kite
    That flies so high
I'm sure it knows
    All birds that fly
And all the clouds
    That cross the sky.
But this one thing
    I've had to say:
I've warned it not
    To fly away
With any wind
    That comes to play.

LELAND M. JACOBS

SHARING THE SWING

When I keep my swing all to myself
I can go as high as our pantry shelf.
When I share my swing with friend
    or brother,
And we take turns at pushing each
    other,
I go like the wind, away up high,
Till it seems as if I could touch the
    sky.

ALICE CROWELL HOFFMAN

BONFIRE SONG

Stand back! Stand back!
    We won't take chances.
Safety first! Safety!
    The bonfire dances.

The flames leap high,
    Reach east, reach west.
Careful! Be careful!
    Safety is best.

LUCRETIA PENNY

HATS

Hats are nice for Sunday School,
    Or going out to tea,

But other times, I think a hat
    Is useless as can be!

Folks say, "My dear, you'll freckle,
    Your skin's so pink and fair!"

But I don't care—I like the feel
    Of breezes in my hair!

FRANCES GORMAN RISSER

ROLLER SKATING

Roller skating
Is such fun;
I go almost faster
Than Bim can run.

He barks so close
I can't go straight;
I think he'd like
To roller skate.

IRENE B. CROFOOT

BIRTHDAYS

If I could choose my birthday,
    I think I'd pick out June,
The month when roses blossom
    And everything's in tune.

I'd have a jolly picnic,
    Out by the little lake,
With pink ice cream and cookies
    And lemonade and cake;

And each child at my picnic
    Should have a red balloon;
But January's children
    Can't have birthdays in June.

WINIFRED C. MARSHALL

IF I HAD A HORSE

If I had a horse,
    I'd like him to be
As white as the whitecaps
    That ride on the sea,

Or I'd like him black
    And little and trim;
Or if he were chestnut
    I'd be proud of him;

I'd like him large,
    A smooth dappled gray,
With big heavy hoofs;
    Or I'd like him bay.

You see it's like this:
    I just wouldn't mind
What was his size
    Or his color or kind;

If I had a horse
    I'd like him so much
I just wouldn't care
    About colors and such.

LUCRETIA PENNY

COASTING

Bobby travels, oh, so fast,
Trees and houses whizzing past.

Once I saw him take a spill
Coasting down McNary's hill.

He didn't seem to mind at all—
Heard him turn to Ned and call,

"Come on—race you to the top!"
Boys and coasters never stop.

DONOVAN MARSHALL

The Photographer

The man who takes my picture knows
Exactly how a child should pose.

He says my chin is 'most too high,
And could I drop it, if I try?

And I'm not smiling just the way
That he had hoped I would today.

He tells me where and how to stand,
And moves my foot, and turns my hand.

And *then* he says I'm wrong, because
I've moved a bit from where I was.

But since I've been myself so long
You'd think I'd know when I was wrong!

ELAINE V. EMANS

AT THE MARKET

When I am at the market,
  I pretend that I've been told
Oranges and bananas
  Are balls and bars of gold;

Eggplants are black diamonds,
  And those watermelons there
Are really giant emeralds,
  Priceless and most rare.

I have great fun in dreaming
  What I would buy and do,
If all of these were mine
  And all of this were true;

But when it's dinnertime again,
  I'm glad enough to see
That vegetables are vegetables
  And fruit are fruits for me.

LUCRETIA PENNY

THE GROCERY STORE

When we are playing grocery store,
  A busy clerk am I.
How shall I wait on all the folk
  Who come my goods to buy?

The people like our grocery store,
  Our shop is neat and bright,
And when I serve the customers
  I'm always most polite.

Some come for eggs, and some for
    milk,
  And some want bread or cheese.
What fun to ask, "Are you next?"
  Or, "What will you have, please?"

LELAND B. JACOBS

BAKESHOP WINDOW

When I go downtown I like to stop
To look in the windows of every shop.
Some are great big ones, and some are
    small,
But the bakeshop window is best of
    all.

It's full of cookies and pies and cakes,
And all the good things the baker
    makes—
Chocolate brownies and lemon tarts,
And little cupcakes shaped like
    hearts;

Lemon and apple and custard pies,
And doughnuts, and cookies of every
    size;
Bread and muffins and biscuits, too—
I wish I could buy them all, I do.

But anyhow, it's lots of fun
Just to stop and *look* at every one.

MARIAN KENNEDY

THE BAKESHOP

If I should find a bakeshop, some
    pleasant summer day,
I'd buy the very nicest things, and
    take them all away.
For Little Brother, I would choose
    a man of gingerbread,
With currant eyes, and currant nose
    and very funny head.

For Grandma, cookies, sweet and
    small, and maybe golden brown,
With scallops all around the edge, the
    finest in the town.
For Daddy, jelly doughnuts, like
    snowballs, round and white.
And then I'd give them to him, when
    he came home at night.

But for my mother, oh, I'm sure, I'd
    have to look around,
And see what else was on the shelves,
    and just what could be found.
And then, at last I'd see it, the lovely
    one I'd take,
With pink-y icing over it, a sort of
    smile-y cake.

ALICE THORN FROST

THE WORLD AROUND US

SCHOOL AGAIN!

Oh, I am so excited, for
  September's come again;

I'm always glad, no matter how
  Much fun the summer's been.

My books are new, my pencils, too;
  My lunch is in my box.

It's such a lark to join my friends
  And go to school in flocks.

My hair is combed, my face is clean;
  Just hear that school bell ring!

Vacation's gone, but I don't care.
  I'm gay as anything.

MARIAN STEARNS CURRY

THE PAINTING LESSON

Red and blue make purple;
Yellow and blue make green.
Such a lot of colors
To paint a lovely scene.

Pink and blue make orchid;
Black and white make gray.
Now I'll dry my brushes
Until another day.

FRANCES GREENWOOD

A SCHOOL PRAYER

Now happy school days once again
Have brought us work and play,
And I am going to try to work
And play in the best way.

So every morning when I wake,
I'll start the day quite right
By thanking God for His great love
And care all through the night.

I'll ask God then to be with me
Through every hour of day,
To make me careful in my work,
And fair and true in play,

To bless each one I love at home,
And all my school friends, too,
And make each day a happy day
For all, the whole year through.

MONICA WILLIAMS

LEARNING

Last year when I was little
  I could only count to three,
And never could remember
  What the next number should be!
But now that I've grown bigger
  I know more than I did then,
For I have been in school a month—
  And I can count to ten!

M. LUCILLE FORD

IN SCHOOL

We learn to write;
We learn to read;
We learn a lot
In school, indeed!

We learn to work
With nails and tools,
And learn to follow
Different rules.

We learn to add
And multiply;
We learn about
The earth and sky.

We learn about
Our many states,
And learn important
History dates.

We learn to plan;
We learn to share;
For birds and pets
We learn to care.

We learn to draw;
We learn to play,
And then we put
Our things away!

VIVIAN G. GOULED

WHEN SCHOOL CLOSES

It's time to stand the books up
  In rows upon the shelves,
And pack the charts and posters
  In neat piles by themselves.

Collect the pens and pencils
  And put the ink away,
For schooltime now is over,
  And every day's for play.

DOROTHY M. BAKER

SCHOOL

To-day we stood beside Corot
And saw the sunlight on the trees;
In high-built Spanish galleons
We sailed across the western seas,
Past strange and lonely islands whose
Inhabitants were cockatoos;

We walked through Hiawatha's land
And helped him built his birch canoe;
We peeped into a robin's nest
To see the eggs all smooth and blue;
And yet there are some folks who
    think
That school is only books and ink!

BLYTHE CLEAVE

CLOSING DAY THOUGHT

I wonder if our schoolbooks are lonely all the day
While through the long vacations in cupboards put away?

I wonder if the blackboard seems rather out of place
Without a single piece of chalk to mark upon its face?

I wonder if the schoolroom is sometimes lonely, too,
While standing bare and empty without a thing to do?

But this we can assure them: When summer days all flee
We'll join them in September and keep them company.

LELAND B. JACOBS

POEMS CHILDREN ENJOY

Going Places

THE WHEEL

How very strangely we should feel
If someone had not made a wheel!
No wagon would have crossed the
    plain,
No puffing engine, no speeding train.

No cart or carriage would there be,
Or roller skates for you and me,
No bicycle or automobile,
If someone had not made a wheel.

JOSEPHINE VAN DOLZEN PEASE

JAMES PALMER

THE LITTLE TRAIN

The little train goes puff! puff! puff!
He knows, if he tries hard enough,
He'll pull the freight cars up the hill.
He says, "I can! I can! I will!

The little train goes ding! ding! ding!
He loves to hear the steel rails sing.
He's pulling very, very hard
Out of the station, out of the yard.

The little train goes choo! choo! choo!
And makes his whistle blow tooo! tooo!
Past the houses, past the mill,
He's puff, puff, puffing up the hill.

MARTHA BATES

TRAVELING

Don't you like a bus ride?
  Don't you like a boat?
Don't you like to watch the waves,
  And feel yourself afloat?
Don't you like a street car,
  Rumbling through the rain?
And don't you like the best of all
  A journey on a train?

J. LILIAN VANDEVERE

THE TRAIN

As the great big train goes chugging
    along
It sings to me this little song,
"*Choo*-choo-choo-choo; *choo*-choo-
    choo-choo;
  Come along with me;
"*Choo*-choo-choo-choo; *choo*-choo-
    choo-choo;
  All the world you'll see.

"Up the hill we'll go, and down the
    other side,
Over the high mountain, through the
    valley wide.
"*Choo*-choo-choo-choo; *choo*-choo-
    choo-choo;
  Woods and lakes you'll see;
"*Choo*-choo-choo-choo; *choo*-choo-
    choo-choo;
  Won't you come with me?"

KATHERINE A. O'BRIEN

I'M AN ENGINE

I'm an engine
  Puffing past,
Puff! Puff! Toot! Toot!
  Going fast!

Smoke is pouring
  From my stack!
I am rushing
  Down the track!

Over mountain,
  Bridge, and plain;
I'm an engine
  With a train!

NONA KEEN DUFFY

THE WISE TRAIN

The train went rushing far away,
  But left the track behind it,
So when it took the road again,
  'Twould know the way to find it!

J. LILIAN VANDEVERE

MEETING THE TRAIN

Down by the station
  As the train comes puffing in,
I like to watch the bustle
  As the people all begin

Rushing down the platform
  With a clatter, clater, clatter,
And I like to see them meeting,
  And hear their merry chatter.

I like to see how quickly
  The commotion settles down.
I certainly am happy
  There's a station in our town.

VIVIAN G. GOULED

ENGINE

Work, little engine,
  Pull us along;
Puff, little engine,
  Puff a gay song!

Work, little engine,
  Pull, pull, pull!
Draw forth cars
  That are full, full, full!

Work, little engine,
  Blizzard or rain;
Puff, little engine,
  Pull the long train!

NONA KEEN DUFFY

I LIKE TO SEE A TRAIN

I like to see
A train pass by,
With smoke
Streaming against the sky!
With wheels
That fast and faster fly!
With engine streaming
Mightily!

I like to see
A train pass by!
I like its whistle's
Far-flung cry!

JOSEPHINE VAN DOLZEN PEASE

FLYING

In early days,
   A joyous sight,
High and higher,
   Flew the kite.

And next was seen,
   So free and fair,
The round balloon
   Upon the air.

But now like mighty birds
   That fly,
The wingéd airplane
   Soars the sky!

JOSEPHINE VAN DOLZEN PEASE

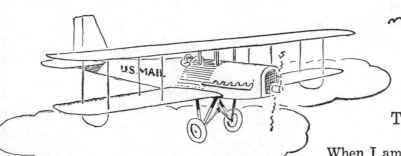

THE EVENING MAIL

I'd like to be a pilot
   Flying the evening mail,
Into storm or starlight
   I'd sail and sail and sail;
And if I flew right over
   A lonely country town,
I think that I would lean out
   And drop a letter down.

IRMA DOVEY

THE AIRPLANE

When I am big I will ride in the sky
And see the clouds go flying by.
I will look below where the tall trees
   grow,
And over the meadows where rivers flow.

I will fly over mountains and ocean's
   shore,
Over fields and houses, and many things
   more.
Like a big, big bird I will soar in the sky,
And folks will say, "There's a plane going
   by!"

FRANCES ARNOLD GREENWOOD

THE AIRPORT

The airport's like a humming hive
With giant ships that dip and dive.
Hear the motors hum and purr!
Hear the great propellers whir!

The ship is ready, stern to prow,
The pilot's in the cockpit now.
Hear the engine music sound!
Now it's rising from the ground—
Rising, rising toward the sky,
Flying, flying swift and high!
Now we cannot hear the roar,
But high above we see it soar.
Soon 'twill vanish from our sight.
Oh, what fun to watch a flight!

The airport's like a humming hive
With giant ships that dip and dive.
Like mighty, buzzing bees they rise
And then return here from the skies.

At night the blazing beacon guides
The pilot till the airplane glides
Straight to port and circles round,
Skimming smoothly to the ground.
What a very busy site
Is the airport, day and night,
Where the ships take off and land!
No other sight is half so grand!
Oh, it is the finest sport—
Watching planes come into port.

MARCELLA HARTMAN

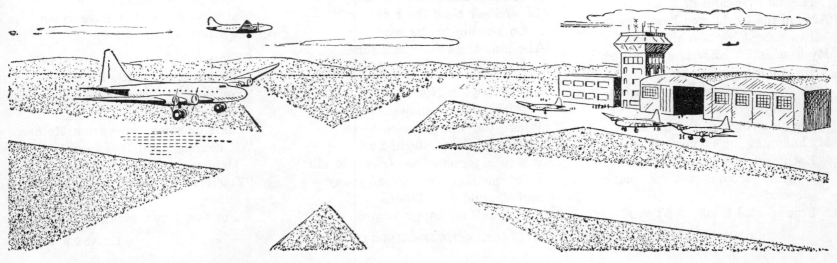

THE LITTLE ESKIMO

Jolly little Eskimo,
Living in his tent of snow,
Wonder how he can be gay
Through the long, long winter day.
Watch him take a merry ride,
With his dogs hitched side by side;
Dressed in fur so very warm,
So no storm can ever harm.

Now he's helping hunt the seal,
Maybe for the evening meal;
Or perhaps a substitute
For his old, now worn-out suit.
There is much that he can do
In that land, the same as you.
He is happy, gay, and strong,
Even though the day is long.

EFFIE CRAWFORD

A FRIENDSHIP BRIDGE

I have a friend I've never seen;
    She lives in far Japan.
We write each other letters
    As often as we can.
It seems to me that letters
    Build a bridge across the sea
O'er which I go to visit her,
    And she comes to visit me!

ALICE CROWELL HOFFMAN

MAKE BELIEVE

My rocking chair is a touring car;
    I'm off for a trip today;
So come with me, and we'll journey
        far—
    Jump in! No fare to pay!
My paper kite is a big airplane;
    It sails over land or sea,
Around the world, and home again—
    I've named my airship "We."
My broomstick horse is a fiery steed;
    He gallops o'er the plain;
Just hear his feet go "Prop-ut-ty
        Prop!"
    See his flying tail and mane!
My humming top's a merry-go-round;
    Each seat has room for two;
We whirl around to the music's
        sound—
    Fine sport, I think; don't you?

ANNA E. OVERTON

GEOGRAPHY

I think geography is *fun!*
    Upon the map, with care,
I trace strange countries, one by one,
    And travel ev'rywhere!

I seek out cities far away,
    Follow down rivers blue,
Trace here a lake, and there a bay,
    Whose names to me are new!

I visit China and Japan;
    I journey down the Rhine!
Then, trav'ling with a caravan,
    A "desert ship" is mine;

I wander in far Timbuctoo;
    In India's plains I trek!
The vales of Greece I wander through,
    And Brazil's rivers check!

To all these places on the map
    I travel, and with ease!
An open book upon my lap,
    I sail the seven seas!

CLARENCE MANSFIELD LINDSAY

A CHILD OF THE VIKINGS

Sigrid lives in Norway,
    Norway of the snows.
Where the sea gull dips and swings,
    That's where Sigrid goes.
There the towering mountains climb,
    The ice gleams blue and cold,
And over all, the Northern Lights
    Flash green and gold.

Sigrid lives in Norway,
    Norway of the snows.
Where the square-sailed rowboats
        glide,
    That's where Sigrid goes.
In summer time the rivers gay
    Go singing to the seas;
The pine trees and the birches
    Have wild flowers at their knees.

Sigrid lives in Norway,
    Norway of the snows.
Where the Vikings used to go
    That's where Sigrid goes.
Where cataracts leap from the cliff
    In splendid showers of spray,
Sigrid, child of Vikings,
    Spends her happy day

BLANCHE JENNINGS THOMPSON

WONDERFUL HOLLAND

I've read in my geography
That Holland's wonderful to see—
With storks at nest in chimneys high
And busy dogcarts clattering by,
With dikes to curb an anxious sea
And windmills turning gracefully,
With houses pink, and tan, and blue,
And merry tunes of the wooden shoe,
With every dooryard clean and neat
And golden yellow cheese to eat,
With field on field of tulips gay
And hyacinths in sweet array.
With all the books I quite agree
That Holland's wonderful to see.

LELAND B. JACOBS

ERRAND

They tell me when the steamers go
    Down to Samarkand,
Or Mozambique, or Colombo,
    Or Somaliland,
The waves that follow in their wakes
    Nightly leap and curl,
And fall in phosphorescent flakes
    Of diamond and pearl!
So I'll go down to Mandalay,
    Or maybe Timbuctoo,
And look and see if what they say
    Is really, really true!

ELAINE V. EMANS

GOING AWAY

When I was busy packing things
    To go for a vacation,
My family all cheerfully
    Kept giving information
On what to take and what to leave
    And just the things to do.
The best advice they gave to me
    I'll pass along to you.

"You won't forget to write to us,"
    Said Sue and Little Brother.
"You surely have your comb and
        brush?"
    This question came from Mother.
"Of course," said Dad in quiet tones
    Of meaningful persuasion,
"You'll take enough good manners,
        too,
    For every new occasion."

LELAND B. JACOBS

POEMS CHILDREN ENJOY

MY SHIP AND I

O it's I that am the captain of a tidy
    little ship,
  Of a ship that goes a-sailing on
    the pond;
And my ship it keeps a-turning all
    around and all about,
But when I'm a little older, I shall
    find the secret out
  How to send my vessel sailing on
    beyond.

For I mean to grow as little as the
    dolly at the helm,
  And the dolly I intend to come
    alive;
And with him beside to help me, it's
    a-sailing I shall go,
It's a-sailing on the water, when the
    jolly breezes blow
  And the vessel goes a divie-divie-
    dive.

ROBERT LOUIS STEVENSON

MAKING MAPS

I love to make maps!
I think it's great fun—
Making the boundaries,
And then, one by one,
Putting in railroads,
And each river bend,
And the tiny towns
Where little roads end.
I draw in mountains,
And often a lake,
And I've even had
Long bridges to make!
I like to do highways,
And when they are drawn
I dream that they take me
Where I've never gone.

ELAINE V. EMANS

THE FISHING FLEET

Into the misty pearly dawn
The fishermen sail away.
Far out from shore they cast their
    nets
Where the deep-sea fishes play.
When evening shadows softly fall
On the surging billows' foam,
Gladly they turn their heavy boats
And sail again for home.

FRANCES ARNOLD GREENWOOD

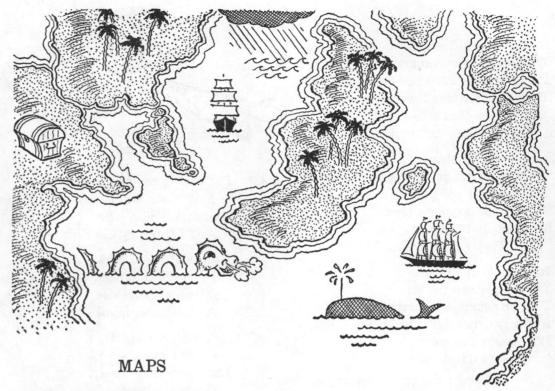

MAPS

I like to study foreign maps;
Some time I'll take a trip, perhaps,

I'd like to hop upon a plane,
And fly to distant, sunny Spain.

I'd like to see the River Nile,
And linger there a little while.

I'd like to see the London Tower
This very month, and day, and hour.

But if I cannot go today,
I'll play that I am going away.

I like to study foreign maps;
Some time I'll go away, perhaps.

EDITH AMELIA SKILES

TRAFFIC LIGHTS

Red light, red light,
What do you say?
I say, "Stop,
And stop right away!"

Yellow light, yellow light,
What do you mean?
I mean "Wait—
Till the light turns green!

Green light, green light,
What do you say?
I say, "Cross!
First look each way!"

Thank, thank you,
Red, yellow, green;
Now I know
What traffic lights mean!

VIVIAN G. GOULED

FRIENDS AROUND THE WORLD

If I should go to London
  I'd find a child like me;
He'd probably play cricket
  And have bread and jam for tea.

If I should go to Holland
  When winter's on the sea,
I'd find the children skating
  Upon the Zuyder Zee.

If I should go to China,
  Or down to Mexico,
I'd find kites or balls or marbles
  Or something I would know.

It's curious to think of it—
  Wherever I might be,
In Spain or France or Russia,
  I'd find children just like me.

BLANCHE JENNINGS THOMPSON

GEOGRAPHY

I met a sailor at the wharf—
  He told me things I never knew

About the seas, and people of
  The countries he has journeyed to.

If I could travel on a ship
  To see lands far away,

I'd know as much geography
  As sailors do, some day.

LAURA SCHNEIDER

IN MEXICO

In Mexico, in Mexico,
The people never hurry.
If things aren't finished quite on time,
The Mexicans don't worry.
"*Mañana*"—that's to-morrow—
    They say in Mexico.

In Mexico, in Mexico,
They like strange things to eat.
The fiery hot red pepper
They think is quite a treat.
Tortillas and tamales
    They eat in Mexico.

In Mexico, in Mexico,
The people are polite;
They're courteous to strangers
And gay from morn to night.
It's pleasant to go traveling
    Down in Mexico.

    BLANCHE JENNINGS THOMPSON

JAPAN

I'm saving my pennies
    And 'most every dime
And nickel with care,
    And I think by the time

I am eighteen years old
    I can go to Japan!
Oh, I'm eager to hire
    A jinrikisha man!

He'll pull me swiftly
    On flying feet
Through every lovely,
    Unusual street.

I'll see the bronze Buddha,
    And kimonos bright;
I'll see the wood pillows
    Folks sleep on at night,

The fans, and the bridges,
    A pink cherry tree!
Oh, Japan has hundreds
    Of things to see!

    ELAINE V. EMANS

MARTHA SUE'S DREAM

I dreamed last night that I went to a
    tea,
    And wore my new blue dress,
But just who the other children were,
    I'm sure you could not guess.

An Eskimo boy in a suit of fur,
    A French girl named Marie,
A Chinese girl with a lovely fan,
    And Gretchen from o'er the sea.

A Japanese boy in a yellow suit,
    A Spanish girl in red,
A little Dutch girl with wooden shoes,
    And a queer cap on her head.

Not one single word did I understand
    Of those they said to me,
But we all could smile, and after a
    while
    Were as friendly as could be.

    WINIFRED C. MARSHALL

A Nautical Ballad

A capital ship for an ocean trip,
    Was the Walloping Window-blind.
No gale that blew dismayed her crew,
    Nor troubled the captain's mind.

The man at the wheel was taught to
    feel
    Contempt for the wildest blow;
And it often appeared—when the
    weather had cleared—
    He had been in his bunk below.

The boatswain's mate was very se-
    date,
    Yet fond of amusement too;

And he played hopscotch with the
    starboard watch,
    While the captain tickled the crew.

And the gunner we had was appar-
    ently mad,
    For he sat on the after-rail
And fired salutes with the captain's
    boots
    In the teeth of the booming gale.

The captain sat on the commodore's
    hat,
    And dined in a royal way,
Off toasted pigs and pickles and figs
    And gunnery bread each day.

The cook was Dutch and behaved as
    such,
    For the diet he gave the crew,
Was a number of tons of hot cross
    buns,
    Served up with sugar and glue.

All nautical pride we laid aside,
    And we cast our vessel ashore,

On the Gulliby Isles, where the Poo-
    Poo smiles
    And the Rumpletum-Bunders roar.

We sat on the edge of a sandy ledge,
    And shot at the whistling bee:
And the cinnamon bats wore water
    proof hats,
    As they danced by the sounding
    sea.

On Rug-gub bark, from dawn till
    dark,
    We fed, till we all had grown
Uncommonly shrunk; when a Chinese
    junk
    Came in from the Torrible Zone.

She was stubby and square, but we
    didn't care,
    So we cheerily put to sea;
And we left the crew of the junk to
    chew,
    The bark of the Rug-gub tree.

    CHARLES E. CARRYL

People We Know

THE POLICEMAN

Honk, honk, sounds a motor car.
"Halt!" says the policeman, "stay where
  you are."
Soon he waves for me and you.
If we had no policemen,
Oh! what would we do!
Crossings might be dangerous for me and
  you.

HARRIET LOVEJOY

THE COBBLER

Rap-tap-tap and tip-tap-too.
Hear the busy cobbler mending a shoe!
Heels and soles for me and you.
If there were no cobblers,
Oh! what would we do!
We would have to run about without a
  shoe!

HARRIET LOVEJOY

THE MILKMAN

Trot, trot, trot upon the street.
Listen to the horses' iron-shod feet
Bringing milk for me and you!
If there were no milkmen,
Oh! what would we do!
Farms are sometimes far from town and
  city, too.

HARRIET LOVEJOY

THE CARPENTER

Rap-tap-tap and tip-tap-tay.
Carpenters are busy over the way
Building homes for me and you.
If there were no builders,
Oh! what would we do!
We would have to live in tents and dug-
  outs, too.

HARRIET LOVEJOY

THE FIREMAN

Clang, clang, down the street they come.
Listen to the engines on the run!
Firemen with their helmets, too.
If we had no firemen,
Oh! what would we do!
Stores and churches might burn down and
  houses, too.

HARRIET LOVEJOY

THE HAMBURGER MAN

The hamburger man is as nice as
    can be;
He's always so jolly and friendly
    to me.
He slashes the bun, and opens it wide;
Then tucks the hot hamburger neatly
    inside;

He spreads on the mustard all even
    and nice;
He puts in the pickles and big onion
    slice;
He sticks through a toothpick to hold
    it shut tight;
In a clean paper bag he twists it up
    right.

Then he says, "Do you know, I doubt
    if you can
Find better hamburgers any place,
    my young man!"

I think, when I grow up, that it would
    be grand
To work every day in a hamburger
    stand!

        REBA MAHAN STEVENS

FIREMEN

Firemen brave,
    Firemen bold,
Come in heat,
    Come in cold.

Firemen working
    All together
Come in any
    Kind of weather,

Trying to keep us
    Safe from harm
When they hear
    The fire alarm.

Where they're needed
    Firemen go.
Quite a debt
    To them we owe!

        NONA KEEN DUFFY

OUR POSTMAN

I like to see him coming,
    The postman dressed in gray,
He's always bright and cheerful,
    No matter what the day.

He waves a cheery greeting,
    When I am in the yard;
Today he brought a letter,
    And yesterday, a card.

It must be quite exciting
    To journey up and down,
And carry cards and letters
    To everyone in town.

        WINIFRED C. MARSHALL

THE BARBERS

Gold locks, and black locks,
    Red locks and brown,
Topknot to love-curl
    The hair wisps down;
Straight above the clear eyes,
    Rounded round the ears,
Snip-snap and snick-a-snick
    Clash the Barber's shears;
Us, in the looking glass,
    Footsteps in the street,
Over, under, to and fro,
    The lean blades meet;
Bay Rum or Bear's Grease,
    A silver groat to pay
Then out a-shin-shan-shining
    In the bright, blue day.

        WALTER de la MARE

FAITHFUL

All winter long the postmen work
    As faithfully as ever.
Come stormy days, with sleet or
    snow,
    These good men fail us never.

Our letter boxes now and then
    Are pillowed all in white.
The postmen brush the pillows off,
    And pack the mail in tight.

They whistle, and sometimes they
    sing,
    While driving here and there,
Glad that they can bring good cheer
    To people everywhere.

        NORMAN C. SCHLICHTER

THE POSTMAN

His letter bag upon his back,
Through wintry wind and summer's heat,
The faithful postman, day by day,
Passes up and down the street.

The people greet him at every door,
With welcome word and friendly face,
Waiting for a package or a picture care,
Or a letter sent from a far-off place.

Through farm and village and busy town,
Faithful he goes upon his way,
With sturdy courage and cheerful heart,
The call of duty to obey.

        JOSEPHINE VAN DOLZEN PEASE

FUTURE PLANS

My brothers and their playmates all
  Keep planning what they'll do
When they are very big and strong
  And educated, too.

John plans to be an engineer,
  And Carl a pastry cook.
And George will go to practice law,
  And Ben will write a book.

Tom says he'll be a carpenter.
  Don wants to be a cop.
And Bob will keep a grocery store
  Or else a candy shop.

They're all so full of business plans
  They won't have time to be
The president in Washington—
  Which leaves that job for me!

HARRIETTE WILBURR PORTER

MR. MINNITT

Mr. Minnitt mends my soles
When I have walked them into holes.

He works in such a funny place
And has a wrinkly, twinkly face.

His hands are brown and hard and
    thin,
His thread goes slowly out and in.

He cannot walk without a crutch—
I like him very, very much.

ROSE FYLEMAN

THE MILKMAN

Early in the morning, when the dawn
    is on the roofs,
You hear his wheels come rolling, you
    hear his horse's hoofs;
You hear the bottles clinking, and
    then he drives away:
You yawn in bed, turn over, and be-
    gin another day!
The old-time dairy maids are dear to
    every poet's heart—
I'd rather be the dairy man and drive
    a little cart,
And bustle round the village in the
    early morning blue,
And hang my reins upon a hook, as
    I've seen Casey do.

CHRISTOPHER MORLEY

From CHIMNEYSMOKE by Christopher Morley. Copyright,
1921, 1949, by Christopher Morley, published by J. B.
Lippincott Company.

THE DENTIST

I'd like to be a dentist with a plate
    upon the door
And a little bubbling fountain in the
    middle of the floor;
With lots of tiny bottles all arranged
    in coloured rows
And a page-boy with a line of silver
    buttons down his clothes.
I'd love to polish up the things and
    put them every day
Inside the darling chests of drawers
    all tidily away;
And every Sunday afternoon when
    nobody was there
I should go riding up and down upon
    the velvet chair.

ROSE FYLEMAN

THE ICE-CREAM MAN

When summer's in the city,
  And brick's a blaze of heat,
The Ice-cream Man with his little
    cart
  Goes trundling down the street.

Beneath his round umbrella,
  Oh, what a joyful sight,
To see him fill the cones with mounds
  Of cooling brown or white:

Vanilla, chocolate, strawberry,
  Or chilly things to drink
From bottles full of frosty-fizz,
  Green, orange, white or pink.

His cart might be a flower bed
  Of roses and sweet peas,
The way the children cluster round
  As thick as honeybees.

RACHEL FIELD

THE FARMER BOY

The farmer boy wears overalls;
  He's sturdy, brown, and strong;
He learns to plow, and ride a horse;
  He hears the wild birds' song.

He goes a-wading in the stream,
  He sees the windmill turn;
He feeds the little squealing pigs,
  And brings in wood to burn.

The farmer boy must tend the ducks
  And help to plant the wheat;
He climbs the trees for luscious fruit
  And gathers berries sweet.

BLOSSOM BENNETT

MR. COGGS

A watch will tell the time of day,
Or tell it nearly, any way,
Excepting when it's overwound,
Or when you drop it on the ground.
If any of our watches stop,
We haste to Mr. Coggs' shop;
For though to scold us he pretends,
He's quite among our special friends.
He fits a dice-box in his eye,
And takes a long and thoughtful spy,
And prods the wheels, and says,
    "Dear, dear!
More carelessness, I greatly fear."
And then he lays the dice-box down
And frowns a most prodigious frown;
But if we ask him what's the time,
He'll make his gold repeater chime.

EDWARD VERRALL LUCAS

THE BAKER

Smiling girls, rosy boys,
Come and buy my little toys;
Monkeys made of gingerbread
And sugar horses painted red.

MOTHER GOOSE

THE GARDENER

The gardener does not love to talk,
He makes me keep the gravel walk;
And when he puts his tools away,
He locks the door and takes the key.

Away behind the currant row
Where no one else but cook may go,
Far in the plots, I see him dig
Old and serious, brown and big.

He digs the flowers, green, red, and
    blue,
Nor wishes to be spoken to.
He digs the flowers and cuts the hay,
And never seems to want to play.

Silly gardener! summer goes,
And winter comes with pinching toes,
When in the garden bare and brown
You must lay your barrow down.

Well now, and while the summer
    stays,
To profit by these garden days
O how much wiser you would be
To play at Indian wars with me!

ROBERT LOUIS STEVENSON

TIRED TIM

Poor tired Tim! It's sad for him.
He lags the long bright morning
    through,
Ever so tired of nothing to do;
He moons and mopes the livelong day,
Nothing to think about, nothing to
    say;
Up to bed with his candle to creep,
Too tired to yawn, too tired to sleep:
Poor tired Tim! It's sad for him.

WALTER de la MARE

AUNT JANE

Aunt Jane's in such a hurry,
She makes us all perplexed;
And when I'm in one moment,
She's always in the next.

When I ride a camel,
She talks of getting down;
And when I start to paddle,
She speaks of boys who drown.

She talks about the doctor,
When cakes are going free;
And when I stroke an elephant,
She says I'll catch a flea.

And she is always thinking
Of dull times to come,
"Time for rest," and "time for bed,"
And "time for going home."

Aunt Jane's in such a hurry,
She makes us all perplexed;
And when I'm in one moment,
She's always in the next.

HERBERT ASQUITH

OUR GRANDMOTHER

Our Grandmother
Bakes home-made bread,
And is very handy
With needle and thread.

She lets out hems,
And darns and patches;
Sets the pills up high,
And hides the matches;

Corrects our grammar,
Calls good manners *art;*
Tells Bible stories
She knows by heart;

Grows African violets
In a dozen pots;
Baby-sits us
And likes us lots!

MILDRED D. SHACKLETT

Chums, We Three

You see, we three,
Fred, Joe and me,
    Is chums.
When I "hullo!"
To Fred and Joe
    They comes.
'Most every day
We go and play
    Somewheres.

If I've a bun
And they has none,
    We shares.
We all can slide;
And Fred can ride
    And swim,
And make a kite!
I think a sight
    Of him.

And Joey, too;—
He helps us do
    Our sums;
Because, you see,
Because, you see,
Joe, Fred, and me
    Is chums.

ARTHUR GUITERMAN

UNCLE FRANK

It's queer about my Uncle Frank,
He sits and figures in a bank,
When he might keep a candy store—
A shining sign above the door.
Or he might keep a big toy shop
With things that fly and skip and
    hop—
With trailer trucks and things that
    crank,
Instead of working in a bank.

MONICA SHANNON

MY GRANDPA

My grandpa is a farmer.
    He has a barn and shed.
He has a lovely orchard,
    With cherries white and red.

He has a flock of chickens,
    He has a Jersey cow,
He has two working horses
    He hitches to a plow.

My grandpa raises carrots,
    Tomatoes, peas, and beans,
Potatoes, corn, and okra,
    Rhubarb, and turnip greens.

He raises squash and melons,
    Persimmons, pears, and cherries,
He raises apricots and plums,
    Some peaches and some berries.

Each day he goes to market,
    And down on Market Street
He sells the things he raises
    For other folks to eat!

NONA KEEN DUFFY

BOBBY BLUE

Sometimes I have to cross the road
    When someone isn't there
Except a man in uniform
    Who takes a lot of care;
I do not call him Officer
    As other people do,
I thank him most politely,
    And call him Bobby Blue.

He's very big, and every one
    Does everything he tells,
The motor-cars with hooters
    And the bicycles with bells;
And even when I cross the road
    With other people too,
I always say as I go by,
    "Good-morning, Bobby Blue."

JOHN DRINKWATER

People We Admire

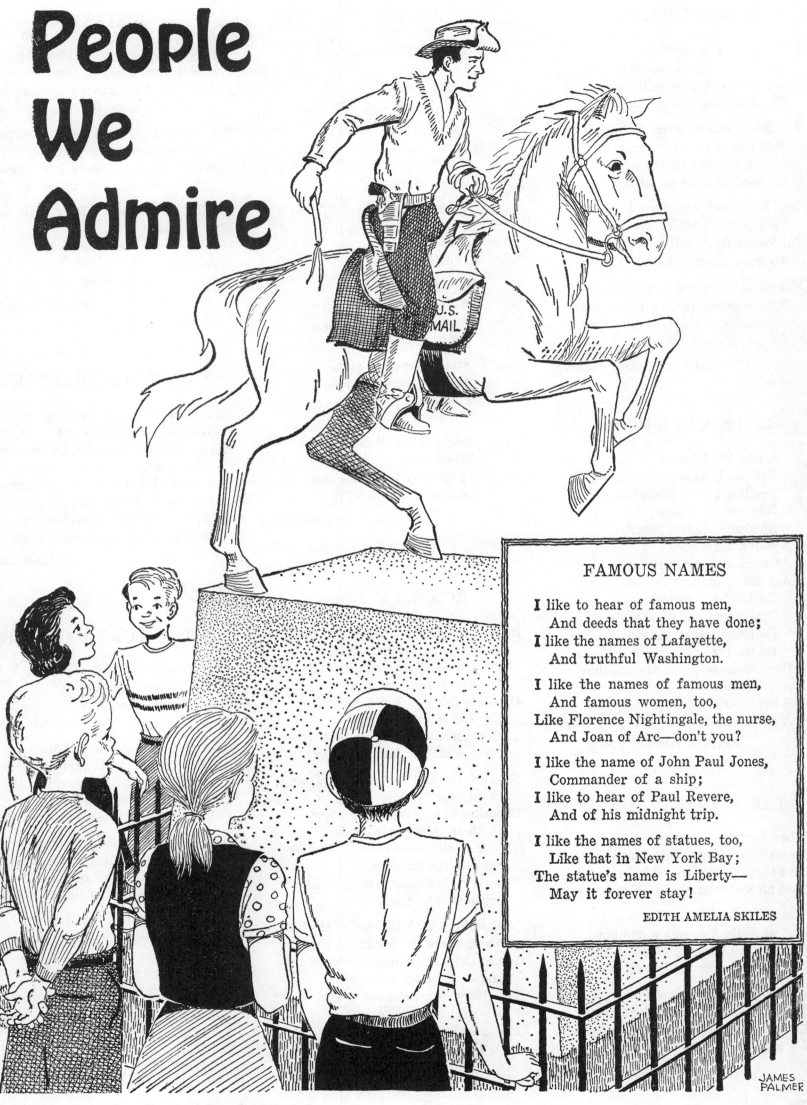

FAMOUS NAMES

I like to hear of famous men,
  And deeds that they have done;
I like the names of Lafayette,
  And truthful Washington.

I like the names of famous men,
  And famous women, too,
Like Florence Nightingale, the nurse,
  And Joan of Arc—don't you?

I like the name of John Paul Jones,
  Commander of a ship;
I like to hear of Paul Revere,
  And of his midnight trip.

I like the names of statues, too,
  Like that in New York Bay;
The statue's name is Liberty—
  May it forever stay!

EDITH AMELIA SKILES

JAMES PALMER

ROGER WILLIAMS

Canonicus is never seen
  With Roger Williams on the shore.
The boats that carried Indian chiefs
  Come drifting by no more.

The quiet man who marked the land
  And gave the settlers each a share
Has long ago put by the books
  He used to keep so fair.

And Mary waits no more for him
  To paddle in beside the quay
All loaded down with silky furs
  To trade across the sea.

But all the free Americans
  Who worship as they please today
Owe homage to the man who built
  On Narragansett Bay.

                    MARGARET GOFF CLARK

LITTLE ABE LINCOLN

  Little Abe Lincoln,
  Tousled head bent low,
  Reading by the firelight's
  Red and fitful glow,
With charcoal for a pencil,
  A shovel for a slate,
At work and not complaining
Against an unkind fate!
  Little Abe Lincoln,
  Dreaming lofty dreams,
  Learning mighty secrets
  By the log fire's beams—
How to shape great dreams into
  A living heart's desire,
Wise, untutored little lad,
  A-sprawl before the fire!

                    FRANCES GORMAN RISSER

THE YOUTHFUL LINCOLN

When Lincoln was a growing boy,
He had few books—not any toy;
He had no lovely shaded light
That he could read beneath at night.

And yet he had the will to learn,
And while the fire logs would burn,
Beside their blaze he often read,
Before he sought his humble bed.

And if perhaps we pause when we
Grow tired, and think of hardships he
Endured, and yet grew kind and strong,
We shall not be discouraged long.

                    MARGARET E. BRUNER

A BOY'S DREAM

You want me to tell you
  The dream I had?
I was visiting Robert
  And Willie and Tad

(Abraham Lincoln's
  Boys, you know),
And it grew dark,
  But I didn't go,

'Cause Lincoln himself,
  In a friendly way,
Smiled and said,
  "You'd better stay!"

So after supper
  We sat and toasted
Our feet at the hearth,
  While apples roasted,

And we cracked nuts,
  And the tall kind man
Told stories better
  Than anyone can.

And the next forenoon
  When my visit was done,
Lincoln called after me,
  "Come again, Son!"

                    ELAINE V. EMANS

ROBERT E. LEE

Soul of the Old South, and her pride!
  Great leader of her sons,
Who fiercely fought and grimly dies
  Amid the flaming guns
Of Gettysburg and red Shiloh!
  Thy countrymen today
The measure of thy greatness know,
  Thou deathless Man in Gray!

"Son of the Old Dominion!" True
  To her at any cost!
Choosing to lead the valiant few,
  Be their cause won or lost!
Thy soul still marches on! We see
  Against the fadeless past
Thy knightly figure, deathless Lee,
  Imperishably cast!

"Mars' Robert!" Chieftain of the host
  Which wore the Southern gray!
Today thou art a nation's boast;
  And shall be so, for aye!
The Stars and Bars are folded now,
  In glory, not in shame!
And a united people bow
  To Lee's immortal name!

                    CLARENCE M. LINDSAY

MISTAKES

I like to hear what Franklin did
  When he was just a boy—
Spent all his birthday pennies for
  A little penny toy.

I like to know that great men, too,
  When they were young like me,
Sometimes made as bad mistakes
  As mine turn out to be.

They learned a lot from their mis-
  takes
  And later on won fame.
Perhaps, if I try very hard,
  I can do the same.

                    CLARA G. CORNELL

A WISH FOR FEBRUARY

The Father of His Country
  Was once a lad like me.
He played and wrestled on the green
  And swung from leafy tree.
But when his country called him
  He put aside his play.
I hope that I, like Washington,
  May serve my land some day!

                    DONOVAN MARSHALL

AS ONE LAD TO ANOTHER

I wish we'd been boys together,
  Abe Lincoln, I really do;
Somehow I cannot help thinking
  I'd have learned so much from you.

You studied under conditions
  That might well have made me
    quail;
In your quest for education
  You knew not a word like *fail*.

And you always made the utmost
  Of everything that you had;
You saw a lot of fun in life
  And you joked when you were sad.

You were ever true and earnest,
  And you saw so much of good
In folks whom others slighted—
  You sensed man's brotherhood.

Though life denies that I should be
  A boy, dear Abe, *with* you,
I still can try with all my might
  To be a boy *like* you.

                    ALICE CROWELL HOFFMAN

Molly Pitcher

'Twas hurry and scurry at Monmouth Town,
　For Lee was beating a wild retreat;
The British were riding the Yankees down,
　And panic was pressing on flying feet.

Galloping down like a hurricane
　Washington rode with his sword hung high,
Mighty as he of the Trojan plain
　Fired by a courage from the sky.

"Halt, and stand to your guns!" he cried.
　And a bombadier made swift reply.
Wheeling his cannon into the tide,
　He fell 'neath the shot of a foeman nigh.

Molly Pitcher sprang to his side,
　Fired as she saw her husband do;
Telling the king in his stubborn pride
　Women like men to their homes are true.

Washington rode from the bloody fray
　Up to the gun that a woman manned.
"Molly Pitcher, you saved the day,"
　He said, as he gave her a hero's hand.

He named her sergeant with manly praise,
　While her war-born face was wet with tears—
A woman has ever a woman's ways—
　And the army was wild with cheers.

KATE BROWNLEE SHERWOOD

Betsy Ross

In a quaint little parlor, once long years ago,
A quaint little lady sat trying to sew
Some bits of bright cloth, each a different hue,
Some red, and some white, and some that were blue.

She'd lay out the red stripes, the white ones between,
Then count with a smile all her loyal thirteen.
She'd measure and baste, then she'd stitch them across,
Would good Betsy, true Betsy, brave Betsy Ross.

Next, a big piece of paper she'd smilingly take,
And skilfully fashion it till she would make
A five-pointed star that just suited, you know;
Then snippity snip would her bright scissors go.

Now would you believe it? In this simple way,
Old Glory was finished one long-ago day.
'Twas made out of bits of bright cloth and soft floss,
By good Betsy, true Betsy, brave Betsy Ross.

CAROLYN R. FREEMAN

A WISH

Oh, I've often wished
  That I could have gone
With Columbus and heard
  "Sail on! Sail on!"
I was born too late
  For Hudson's "Half Moon,"
Or to go exploring
  With Daniel Boone.

I was much too young
  Of course, when I heard
That brave men were wanted
  To go with Dick Byrd!
Oh, I certainly hope
  Someday there will be
A great new adventure
  Waiting for *me!*

ELAINE V. EMANS

WHEN COLUMBUS WAS A BOY

A harbor in a sunny, southern city;
Ships at their anchor, riding in the
    lee;
A little lad, with steadfast eyes, and
    dreamy,
Who ever watched the waters lov-
    ingly.

A group of sailors, quaintly garbed
    and bearded;
Strange tales, that snared the fancy
    of the child;
Of far-off lands, strange beasts, and
    birds, and people,
Of storm and sea-fight, danger-filled
    and wild.

And ever in the boyish soul was ring-
    ing
The urging, surging challenge of the
    sea,
To dare,—as these men dared, its
    wrath and danger,
To learn,—as they, its charm and
    mystery.

Columbus, by the sunny, southern
    harbor,
You dreamed the dreams that man-
    hood years made true;
Thank God for men—their deeds have
    crowned the ages—
Who once were dreamy lads like you.

HELEN L. SMITH

King Bruce and the Spider

King Bruce of Scotland flung himself
    down
  In a lonely mood to think;
'Tis true he was monarch, and wore
    a crown,
  But his heart was beginning to
    sink.

For he had been trying to do a great
    deed,
  To make his people glad;
He had tried and tried, but couldn't
    succeed?
  And so he became quite sad.

He flung himself down in low des-
    pair,
  As grieved as man could be;
And after a while as he pondered
    there,
  "I'll give it all up," said he.

Now, just at that moment a spider
    dropped,
  With its silken, filmy clue;
And the King, in the midst of this
    thinking stopped
  To see what the spider would do.

'Twas a long way up to the ceiling
    dome,
  As it hung by a rope so fine,
That how it would get to its cobweb
    home
  King Bruce could not divine.

It soon began to cling and crawl
  Straight up, with strong en-
    deavor;
But down it came with a slippery
    sprawl,
  As near to the ground as ever.

Up, up it ran, not a second to stay,
  To utter the least complaint,
Till it fell still lower, and there it lay
  A little dizzy and faint.

It's head grew steady—again it went,
  And traveled a half yard higher;
'Twas a delicate thread it had to
    tread,
  And a road where its feet would
    tire.

Again it fell and swung below,
  But again it quickly mounted;
Till up and down, now fast, now slow,
  Nine brave attempts were counted.

"Sure," cried the King, "That foolish
    thing

Will strive no more to climb;
When it toils so hard to reach and
    cling,
  And tumbles every time."

But up the insect went one more;
  Ah me! 'tis an anxious minute;
He's only a foot from his cobweb
    door,
  On, say, will he lose or win it?

Steadily, steadily, inch by inch,
  Higher and higher he got;
And a bold little run at the very last
    pinch
  Put him into his native cot.

"Bravo, bravo!" the King cried out;
  "All honor to those who try;
The spider up there, denied despair;
  He conquered, and why shouldn't
    I?"

And Bruce of Scotland braced his
    mind,
  And gossips tell the tale,
That he tried once more as he tried
    before,
  And that time did not fail.

Pay goodly heed, all ye who read,
  And beware of saying, "I CAN'T";
'Tis a cowardly word, and apt to lead
  To idleness, folly, and want.

Whenever you find your heart despair
  Of doing some goodly thing,
Con over this strain, try bravely
    again,
  And remember the spider and
    King!

ELIZA COOK

Our Country

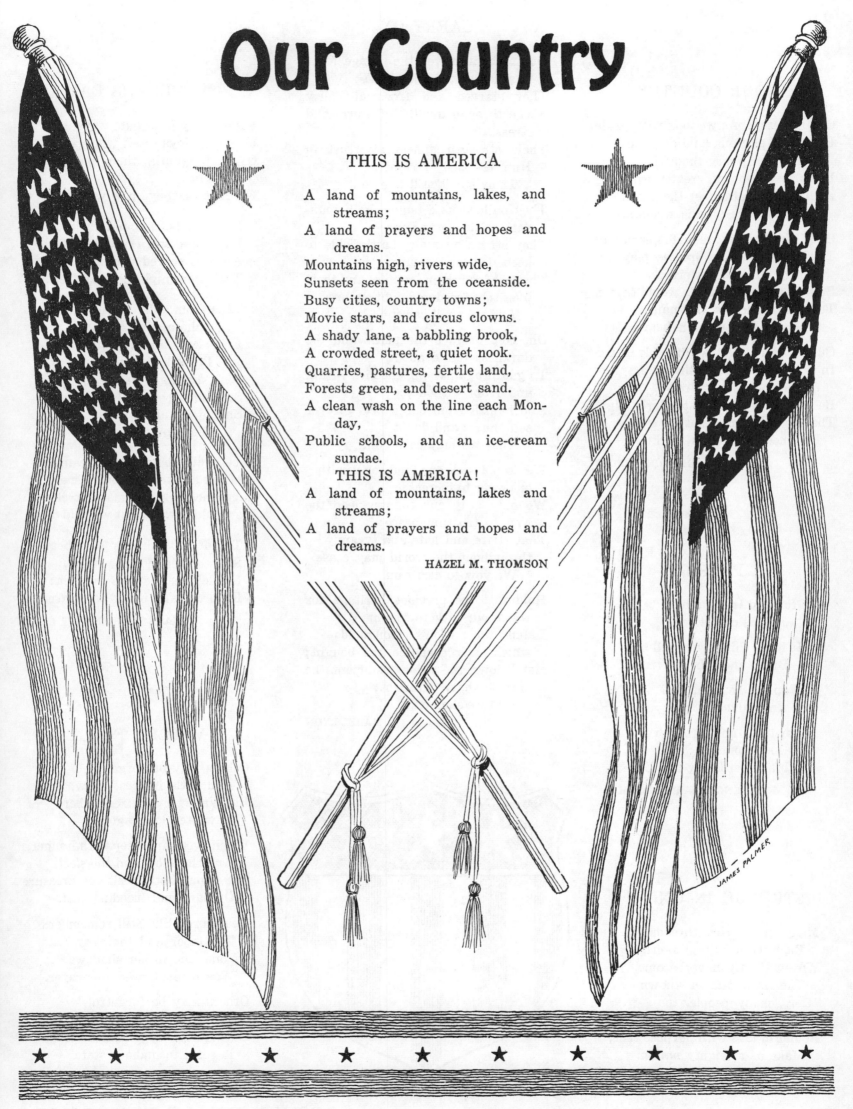

THIS IS AMERICA

A land of mountains, lakes, and
  streams;
A land of prayers and hopes and
  dreams.
Mountains high, rivers wide,
Sunsets seen from the oceanside.
Busy cities, country towns;
Movie stars, and circus clowns.
A shady lane, a babbling brook,
A crowded street, a quiet nook.
Quarries, pastures, fertile land,
Forests green, and desert sand.
A clean wash on the line each Mon-
  day,
Public schools, and an ice-cream
  sundae.
THIS IS AMERICA!
A land of mountains, lakes and
  streams;
A land of prayers and hopes and
  dreams.

HAZEL M. THOMSON

TO OUR COUNTRY

Our Country! As we look with pride
Upon this glorious land so wide,
  O may our every thought
Be to make you of greater worth,
An upright nation on the earth,
  Where justice true is wrought.

Our Country! As we watch each day
Thy banner in the breezes play,
  O may our every word
Be such as honest hearts would frame,
To bring honor to thy name,
  Where'er that name is heard.

Our Country! As we humbly share
In thy protection and thy care,
  O may our every deed
Be done to hold right standards high,
That freedom may not be a lie,
  But meet a people's need.

                    M. LUCILLE FORD

A PATRIOT

How old is a patriot?
  Just as old as you,

If in all things you will be
  Brave and fair and true.

Who can be a patriot?
  Any child can try,

For truth and strength and
    self control
  Make heroes by and by.

        KATE ENGLEHARDT CLARK

STRENGH IN UNION

Many, many tiny threads,
  Each weak if used alone,
Woven tightly have become
  The finest banner known
Many, many people, too,
  Of ev'ry walk and station,
Bound in love with purpose true,
  Make us a mighty nation.

        ALICE CROWELL HOFFMAN

CARRY ON

Our fathers braved the savage foe;
  they tamed the wilderness;
They starved and froze at Valley
Forge through months of storm and
  stress,
Their strength upheld by trust in
  Him, the God of righteousness.
    Their spirit still lives on.

They builded us a temple with foun-
  dations strong and sure;
They strove on many battlefields to
  keep our land secure;
They pledged their fortunes and their
  lives that freedom might endure,
    And we shall carry on.

Oh, help us face the perils and the
  darkness round about,
To guard against our enemies within
  and from without;
And banish from our hearts forever
  selfishness and doubt,
    That we may carry on.

We do not seek our lands or wealth
  or power to increase;
We only pray our country lead the
  way to trusting peace;
That strife and hate and tyranny
  throughout the world may cease.
    We vow to carry on.

Hold fast the precious heritage for
  which our fathers fought;
Defend the nation's strongholds
  which their sacrifice has bought;
Hand down the noble testament the
  patriots have wrought;
    And we shall on.

                    MABEL LYON

VETERANS DAY

Flags today in tribute wave
For those loyal ones who gave
Of their youth, their hopes, their
    might
For a cause they knew was right.

  Morning bells sound their call.
  Pause and say a prayer for all—
  All who served valiantly
  That men might be ever free.

  Taps from quiet Arlington
      Echo again.
  Ever keep in memory
      Peace-loving men,
  Who, hating tyranny,
  Struggled that liberty
  Should for all time be
      Won for every land.

Once again the challenge came,
And the answer was the same.
Eager hearts have made it clear
We would guard what we hold dear.

  Toll of bells, drums' slow beat—
  Silence falls in every street.
  In each heart swells the plea:
  Keep us safe, but keep us free!

        KATE ENGLEHARDT CLARK

VALLEY FORGE

Others may be forgetful,
  And little interest show,
But Valley Forge remembers
  A winter long ago

When eyes sank deep with hunger,
  And the snow and the sleet.
Her ground still feels the pressure
  Of bare and bleeding feet.

Yea more. She still remembers
  The labor and the care
Of one who in her shadows
  Was often bowed in prayer.

Others may be forgetful,
  Now that the land is great,
But Valley Forge remembers
  It costs to make a state.

        CLARENCE EDWIN FLYNN

THIS LAND IS OURS

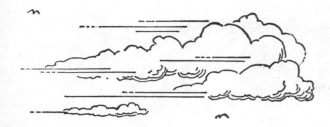

This land is ours;
  Its golden grains,
Its mountain peaks,
  And fruited plains.

This land is ours
  To have and hold;
Its wells of oil,
  Its veins of gold.

Its sturdy schools,
  Its churches fine;
Its forest plots
  Of spruce and pine.

Its waterfalls,
  Its caps of snow
Its ferns and moss
  Where brooklets flow!

Its surfaced roads
  On which we ride
Stretch miles across
  The countryside.

This land is ours;
  Its sun and shade,
Where democratic
  Codes are made.

This land is ours;
  Its fields of corn
Where gentlemen
  Of strength are born.

This land is ours
  To love and cherish,
To guard, that freedom
  Does not perish!

NONA KEEN DUFFY

THERE'LL ALWAYS BE AMERICA

There'll always be America
  To stretch from sea to sea,
A land of liberty and love,
  A land so brave and free!

Let's help to build America,
  A land for future years,
A place where people may be safe,
  And free from grief and fears.

There'll always be America—
  Let's build her to endure,
Let's build for future citizens,
  And liberty ensure.

Let's help to build America,
  Let's serve her every cause,
Let's keep democracy alive,
  And help uphold her laws!

NONA KEEN DUFFY

AMERICA

America, our Fatherland,
  We're loyal, brave, and true.
We love our country's valiant flag
  Of red and white and blue.

We love the freedom that we share
  From sea to shining sea.
We pledge our lives in full support
  Of our democracy.

Our continent is bountiful,
  With fruit and grain to spare;
Our land is blest with fertile soil
  And plenty everywhere.

We're all your loyal citizens,
  Our own dear Fatherland;
We love your verdant valleys fair,
  Your mountain peaks so grand.

We love our people and our land,
  Our homes and cities fair;
We love our own United States,
  In which we have a share.

NONA KEEN DUFFY

I LOVE AMERICA

I love America:
  Her lakes and rolling seas,
Her wooded mountainsides,
  Her giant redwood trees!

I love America:
  Her fields of yellow grain,
Her villages and farms
  That stretch across the plains.

I love America:
  Her mountains bleak and grand,
Her highways smooth and wide
  That circle all the land.

I love America:
  She has so much to give—
Her churches, schools, and all
  Her homes where children live.

I love America:
  Her factories and planes,
Her rafts and boats and tugs,
  Her ships and streamlined trains.

I love America:
  From East to shining West,
For all she means to me;
  I love my country best!

NONA KEEN DUFFY

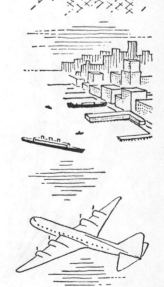

LUCKY STARS

I've often heard grown people say:
  "I thank my lucky stars!"
And wondered what they really
    meant,
  For Jupiter and Mars
Seemed much too far away, to me,
  For blessings to bestow.
But what they mean by "lucky stars"
  I think at last I know.

I see them shining every day—
  Morning, noon, and night.
Their whiteness gleams from out the
    blue,
  Brave champions of right,
The fifty stars in nine straight
    rows—
  There's one for every state.

They stand for union, purity,
  For courage, free from hate,
For honesty and freedom
  Of speech and of the press,
For all the many principles
  Our nation's laws express.

So now, I, too, can truly say:
  "I thank my lucky stars!"
And I will try to live my life
  So that it never mars
The qualities they stand for.
  The Banner of the Free
Shall always fly in freedom
  With lucky stars for me.

CARMEN LAGOS SIGNES

A SONG FOR OUR FLAG

Sing for the flag,
Our country's flag!
We love its stripes and stars!
The stars of white on a field of blue,
The white and crimson bars.

Sing for the flag,
Our country's flag!
Emblem of liberty!
It floats above our beauteous land,
Protecting you and me.

Sing for the flag,
Our country's flag!
Oh, may it ever be
A brave and gallant symbol
Of truth and liberty!

RACHEL M. ROLSHEIM

OLD GLORY

The Star-Spangled Banner: Wherever it
    gleams,
At home or abroad, we behold, as it
    streams,
The symbol of liberty—message of hope
And freedom and light to the captives
    who grope
In the darkness, where tyranny reigns,
    iron-heeled,
And courage to those who would other-
    wise yield.
Our Star-Spangled Banner! To thee we'll
    be true,
Majestic Old Glory—the Red, White, and
    Blue.

In sacred emblazonry all may behold
Our liberty shining in every bright fold.
No fiery-eyed eagle or lion we see,
But only the beacon of loved liberty.
O'er Washington's army it blended its
    charms;
Before it Burgoyne once laid down his
    arms;
The flag floating o'er them, the patriots
    cheered;
The enemy shrank, for Old Glory they
    feared.

On the highlands at West Point its bright
    colors flew;
It floated o'er old Fort Montgomery, too.
When Arnold our fair country tried to
    betray,
Before it his treachery melted away.
Our army it cheered on its famous retreat;
To Valley Forge soldiers it brought cour-
    age sweet:
The Stars and the Stripes, as it floated on
    high,
Brought smiles to their lips and a tear to
    their eye.

At Trenton, the ice-rolling river it crossed;
At last over Yorktown in victory tossed.
Our immortal banner of red, white, and
    blue,
The blood of the brave was invested in
    you!
And we will defend you, come weal or
    come woe,
On land, on the sea, and wherever we go;
In health and prosperity, drought or in
    flood,
Because you were bought with the patriot's
    blood.

ELLA KILLAM BENNETT

POEMS CHILDREN ENJOY

Holidays
Through the Year

THE NEW YEAR

A glad New Year, each day a page
    As fresh and white as snow;
Cold winter, and waking spring,
    And summer, warm and slow;
Bright autumn, jolly Halloween,
    Thanksgiving, Christmas cheer—
The record of a happy time,
    A beautiful New Year!

MARGARET OLESON

SNOW MAN'S VALENTINE

I have a jolly snow man,
    The best I've ever had.
I'm giving him a valentine
    That ought to make him glad.
For though he's very handsome
    And sound in every part,
I noticed only yesterday
    He hasn't any heart.
So quickly with my scissors
    And paper red and fine
I've made a fancy little heart:
    My snow man's valentine!

                    LELAND B. JACOBS

SUSY'S VALENTINE

Susy made valentines
For Dick and Paul and May.
She painted on some paper lace
Flowers bright and gay.
She cut some little scarlet hearts
And fastened them with glue;
Then on each one she wrote,
"My Valentine! For you!"

Susy mailed the valentines
To Dick and Paul and May.
She gave them to the postman
For St. Valentine's own day.
He took them to her little friends,
As postmen always do;
Then when he came to her house,
He left some for Susy, too.

                    SOLVIEG PAULSON RUSSELL

A SPECIAL VALENTINE

"It's time to make my valentines,'
    To Mother I had said.
"I must have ribbons and I'll need
    Some slices of your bread."

"What will you make?" my mother
    asked;
    I did not tell her, though.
"You'll be surprised," was my reply,
    "But you'll be pleased, I know."

Out to the kitchen then I ran,
    And soon I'd finished there
My strange new kind of valentine
    That, none the less, was fair.

I hung my valentines outdoors
    All tied with ribbons red,
And snowflakes made a dainty lace
    For each white heart of bread.

When Mother saw what I had made,
    She smiled and said, "How fine!
Now all the hungry little birds
    Will have a valentine!"

                    LELAND B. JACOBS

THE VALENTINE

'Twas in the sunny Southland,
    Where birds and flowers are gay,
That Mr. Robin Redbreast
    Went wooing one bright day.

He sought a fair young robin,
    So modest and so shy,
And sang to her his love song,
    In notes both clear and high.

"If you will be my sweetheart,
    My little Valentine,
Together we will travel
    Throughout the glad springtime.

"We'll journey to the northward
    And there we'll build our nest,
We'll be the first arrivals
    And have the very best.

"So tell me, dear Miss Robin,
    Your love is true as mine,
That you will be my sweetheart,
    My little Valentine."

                    ESTELLA M. SCHARF

A VALENTINE

A valentine—and it is mine;
    It tells a secret, too.
See underneath its lacy frills—
    "I send my love to you."

                    ADA CLARK

VALENTINE FOR GRANNY

Dear Granny, here's a valentine;
    I made it just for you;
This rosebud and this paper lace
    Are fastened tight with glue.

This little heart I painted red,
    These flowers I made blue,
And Granny, look, here are the words,
    "Dear Granny, I love you."

                    SOLVEIG PAULSON RUSSELL

VALENTINE!

I made a snow man yesterday
So jolly, fat, and fine;
I pinned a red heart on his chest
And named him "Valentine."

Last night a warm, sweet breeze blew
    by,
And stole his heart so gay;
My snow man melted on the spot
And quickly ran away!

                    FRANCES GORMAN RISSER

ST. VALENTINE'S DAY

St. Valentine's Day is a gay time;
    We're busy with scissors and paste;
And oh, there are comings and goings,
    With never a moment to waste.

There's Jane writing verses, and Jill
    tying bows,
    And Jack cutting little gold darts;
While Betty is pasting with all of
    her might,
    Tom's printing, "I love you," on
    hearts.

Quite soon they'll be finished, and
    then for the fun
    Of rapping and running away;
Oh, really, I think the best time
    Is good old St. Valentine's Day!

                    MARION DOYLE

OUR VALENTINE

I know the nicest valentine
You ever could discover,
With eyes of blue and curls of brown,
And dimples just all over.

This pretty little valentine
Was sent last year to Mother;
Today he is just one year old—
My little baby brother.

ALICE Du BOIS

JACK FROST'S VALENTINE

Wee Jack Frost made for his friends
  A charming valentine—
Dainty flowers of finest lace
  Of fairy-like design:
Laid the present on the window,
  Quickly ran away,
And thought that it would bring to us
  A message sweet and gay.

Mr. Sun said, "Well, just look!"
  And laughed full merrily;
Never seemed to understand
  'Twas left for you and me!
And, because he did not know
  That it was yours and mine,
He melted it to crystal dew
  And *drank* our valentine!

SARAH GRAMES CLARK

THE ONLY ONE

Crimson hearts, and charming laces,
Pretty, smiling, dimpled faces,
Dainty bits of verse and rhymes,
Oh, what pretty valentines!

I must buy one for my mother.
Of fair ladies there's no other
That I love so much, you see;
She's the only girl for me.

CAROLYN R. FREEMAN

IF WERE A VALENTINE

Wish I were a valentine, valentine,
    valentine,
  Wish I were a valentine, shiny and
    new.

If I were a valentine, valentine,
    valentine,
  I would be your valentine, loving
    and true.

If I were a valentine, valentine,
    valentine,
  If I were a valentine, what would
    I do?

I'd fly away, fly away, fly away,
    fly away,
  If I were a valentine, I'd fly to you.

KATHLEEN EILAND

Valentine Land

One day as I was walking
I met a little man.
His eyes were bright and blue;
His coat was red and tan.

He said, "How do you do, Miss?
Now would you like to see
A lovely land where valentines
Grow right upon a tree?"

I said, "I'd be delighted."
He said, "Then come with me.
It's right inside this garden wall.
Here is my magic key."

He took out from his pocket
A key that seemed quite small,
But, as he gently shook it,
It stretched out long and tall.

I did not see a keyhole
Or any door at all,
Of course one must have been there,
For it opened up the wall.

We stepped into a wondrous land
Where valentines *did* grow.
They hung in beautiful festoons
From lace trees, row on row.

There were blue for-get-me-nots,
And there were roses red.
And tiny cupid bumblebees
Kept droning overhead.

"Here Hearty, Here!" the small man
    cried,
And, quicker than a wink,
There trotted out a heart-shaped dog
Whose hair was rosy pink.

His heart-shaped ears were cocked
    up high,
His heart-shaped eyes would blink,
His heart-shaped mouth said, "Bow-
    wow-wow,"
Or "Howdy, folks," I think.

The small man stroked the little dog
And tweaked his whiskers red;
Then he turned his glance to me
And smilingly he said,

"This is the Land of Valentines,
And I'm the duke, my dear,
And you're the only little child
Who ever entered here.

"Come walk along this little path—
It's paved with hearts, you see.
There, beyond that wooded hill,
Is Heart House—home to me,

"And to my gentle duchess,
The fairest in the land.
She is the loveliest valentine,
As you will understand."

We wandered down the pathway;
At Heart House we had "tea,"
But it seemed just like lemonade
In heart-shaped cups to me.

The duchess was so dainty
In her gown of softest blue;
She urged me to stay longer,
And I really wanted to.

Now I don't think this was a dream
And yet I cannot say;
I'd like to see that land again,
But I have lost the way.

SOLVEIG PAULSON RUSSELL

ST. VALENTINE

A dear old man,
As I've heard tell,
Had many friends
He loved very well.
  He walked with children,
  Up and down dell—
  He played with them,
  And stories would tell.
    Now when he was sick,
    This dear old man
    Couldn't play or visit,
    So he had a fine plan.
      Friendly letters he wrote,
      And sent by the birds,
      From his opened windows.
      (That's what I've heard.)
        And those kind letters—
        Messages of love—
        Were from Mr. Valentine,
        And his postmen were doves.

MABEL WALTER

A NATION'S HERO

The flags fly, the bands play;
Give him the honor due
To one who served his country well,
A leader brave and true.
First in defense and first in peace;
In our hearts, as of yore,
He holds first place, George Washington,
Our hero, evermore.

WINIFRED C. MARSHALL

LINCOLN

Born in grinding poverty,
  Exposed to frontier strife,

Poor in things material,
  But, oh, how rich his life!

May we learn the lesson that
  This thought of Lincoln brings;

Life never can be measured well
  By its material things.

ALICE CROWELL HOFFMAN

GEORGE WASHINGTON

I wonder if George Washington
Was very fond of books,

And if he liked to hunt and fish,
And wade in little brooks.

I wonder if his pocket bulged
Like mine with precious things,

With marbles, cookies, tops, and balls,
And nails, and glass, and strings.

I wonder if he whistled tunes
While mending broken toys—

My father says George Washington
Was much like other boys.

WINIFRED C. MARSHALL

YOU CANNOT TELL

When Lincoln and George Washington
  Were little boys like me,
They never thought when they grew
  up
  That they would ever be

The President; and boys and girls
  Over books would pore
That told the way each worked and
  played
  So many years before.

Perhaps *I* should be careful,
  And live my boyhood well,
For sometime they might read of
  me—
  You really cannot tell!

DAISY JENNEY CLAY

FEBRUARY THOUGHTS

When I've been reading stories
Of a long time ago,

I look around at all the friends
And playmates that I know.

I think, "Well, maybe Jim will be
A president some day;

And perhaps people years from now
Will read of Ann or Kay."

Each one of them might render
Some service fine and true;

For Washington and Lincoln
Once were children, too.

And if they grew to be great men
And shaped our country's ways,

We children who are gowing now
May serve in future days.

So we who love our country
Should strive each day to be

Wise and worthy leaders
Of the land where men are free.

SOLVEIG PAULSON RUSSELL

ON LINCOLN'S BIRTHDAY

On Lincoln's birthday
  I try to walk
Straighter and taller,
  And try to talk

To the folks I meet
  In the kindly way
Lincoln would do
  If he lived today.

On Lincoln's birthday
  It seems I hear
These words on the wind,
  Steady and clear:

"Fourscore and seven
  Years ago...."
And around my heart
  Creeps a warm bright glow.

On Lincoln's birthday
  I sometimes plan
The person I'll be
  When I'm a man;

And the picture I dream
  That never grows dim
Is of myself
  Being much like him!

ELAINE V. EMANS

POEMS CHILDREN ENJOY

BUD O'MALLY

Bud O'Mally, with his very red hair,
    And his very, very, very green tie,
Sure! he was a pleasing sight
    For good St. Patrick's eye;

Sweet Miss Tulip thought him
    A new posy, without doubt;
And all agreed who saw him
    That Bud had blossomed out.

CAROLYN SHAW RICE

ERIN'S ISLE

There's a charmin' bit o' country
    That is known as Erin's Isle,
Where merry winds make music
    And the fairies dance the while.

'Tis the land of the shillalah,
    Of the shamrock and hilleen,
And boys and girls show loyalty
    A-wearing of the green.

Sure, "The Wearing of the Green" is
        sung,
    Wherever there is found
A loyal son of Erin's Isle
    The whole wide world around;

So, although 'tis not our country,
    We'll join with theirs our lay,
And sing "The Wearing of the Green"
    On good St. Patrick's Day.

BEULAH SISSON

ST. PATRICK'S DAY

Oh, don't forget that blustery March
    Brings in St. Patrick's Day,
When all of Ireland's children
    Sing a blithe and gladsome lay,
And, scattered all about the world,
    The color emerald green
In honor of St. Patrick
    On the seventeenth is seen.

SARAH GRAMES CLARK

ST. PATRICK'S GREEN

Oh, I love to see the shamrocks
    Boys wear March seventeen,
And I love the girl's green ribbons,
    And bits of evergreen;
For they stand for brave St. Patrick,
    So fearless and so good,—
Oh! the Irish ought to love him,
    Just as everybody should!

BERTHA E. BUSH

Wearing of the Green

Oh! Paddy, dear, and did you hear
    the news that's going round,
The shamrock is forbid by law to
    grow on Irish ground;
St. Patrick's day no more we'll keep,
    His color can't be seen,
For there's a bloody law agin' the
    Wearin' o' the Green;

I met with Napper Tandy and he tuk
    me by the hand,
And he said "How's poor old Ireland,
    and how does she stand?"
She's the most distressful country,
    that ever you have seen;
They're hanging men and women
    there for wearing of the green.

Then since the color we must wear
    is England's cruel red,
Sure Ireland's sons will ne'er forget
    the blood that they have shed;
You may take the shamrock from
    your hat, and cast it on the sod,
But 'twill take root and flourish still,
    though underfoot 'tis trod;

When the law can stop the blades of
    grass from growing as they grow,
And when the leaves in summer time
    their verdure dare not show;
Then I will change the color I wear
    in my caubeen,
But 'till that day, I'll stick for aye
    to wearing of the green.

But if at last our color should be
    torn from Ireland's heart,
Her sons with shame and sorrow
    from the dear old soil will part;
I've heard whisper of a country that
    lies far beyond the sea,
Where rich and poor stand equal, in
    the light of freedom's day;

Oh, Erin must we leave you, driven
    by the tyrant's hand,
Must we ask a mother's welcome
    from a strange but happy land?
Where the cruel·cross of England's
    thralldom never shall be seen,
And where, in peace, we'll live and
    die, awearing of the green.

IRISH AIR

The Easter Egg Hunt

Early Easter morning,
With Dorothy and Don,
I went hunting Easter eggs
Upon the grassy lawn.

We searched in nooks and corners,
And in the rose bed, too,
And soon had filled our baskets
With red and green and blue.

I showed mine to my speckled hen,
And do you know, my dear,
She seemed to like her plain eggs best
And think that mine were queer.

WINIFRED C. MARSHALL

TO THE RAIN

Rain, rain, stay away,
Do not come on Easter Day;
You will spoil my fine new hat,
With the posies on it, that
Mother purchased in the shop.
Do not rain a single drop;
On three hundred sixty-four
Other days, rain, you may pour.

GLADYS LLOYD

AN EASTER PUZZLE

This morning, what do you suppose
  I found beside my door?
A nest of colored Easter eggs—
  Five or six or more.

I asked my own pet bunny,
  Who seems to love me so,
To tell me where they came from;
  I thought perhaps he'd know.

Yet not a single word he said,
  Though twice he blinked his eyes;
But I believe he really knows
  Because he looked so wise.

ALICE Du BOIS

EASTER EGGS

Sing a song of Easter eggs—
  Betty counted eight,
Hidden in a grassy nook,
  By the garden gate;

Two beneath the lilac bush,
  Near the pansy bed;
Bob gave her a purple one;
  She gave Bob a red;

Four beneath a wild rosebush,
  Growing in the yard.
Let's help Betty count her eggs;
  It will not be hard.

WINIFRED C. MARSHALL

THE NEW BONNET

I have a new bonnet
A pretty new bonnet,
A new yellow bonnet
To wear on May Day.

There are daffodils on it,
And flutes and frills on it.
On May Day I'll don it;
Oh, won't I be gay!

JULIA POWELL

AN EASTER PARTY

'Twas early springtime when a gay
  rabbit said,
  "I must buy a new hat to wear on
    my head,
And color some eggs blue, yellow,
  and red,
  For the children's party on
    Easter."

The morning was bright and the
  mother hen's call
  Awoke every chick, so sleepy and
    small.
"You must hurry and dress," she
  said, "one and all,
  For the children's party on
    Easter."

The crocuses bright and the daffodils
  Were dressed in pure gold, with
    ruffles and frills,

And lilies snow white peeped from
  low window sills,
  For the children's party on
    Easter."

The robin had charge of events for
  the day;
  He wore a red vest all spangled and
    gay.
So busy he was, half in work, half in
  play,
  For the children's party on
    Easter."

The children were there looking
  cheerful and bright,
  Voices all ringing in shouts of de-
    light.
Each ready to frolic from morning till
  night
  At that children's party on Easter.

CLARA EMOGENE BOWEN

POEMS CHILDREN ENJOY

EXPLAINING IT TO DOLLY

I've tried my very best to be
    As good to you, dear dolly,

As Mother dear has been
    To Bud and me and Polly—

But if I have not measured up
    In one way or another,

You must remember it's quite hard
    To be as good as Mother.

ALICE CROWELL HOFFMAN

MOTHER'S DAY

I'd like to buy Mother
Some perfume.
I'd like to buy Mother
A ring,
But I am too small
To have money,
And so I can't *BUY* her
A thing.

But Mother once told me
She's happy
Just seeing me laughing
And gay—
So I'll be especially merry
When Mother's Day
Comes,
In May.

VIVIAN G. GOULED

MEASURELESS

There are miles to measure countries,
    There are bushels, too, for wheat;

There are fathoms for the ocean,
    Degrees to measure heat.

There are years to measure ages,
    Light-years for stars above,

But no way has been discovered
    To measure mother love.

ALICE CROWELL HOFFMAN

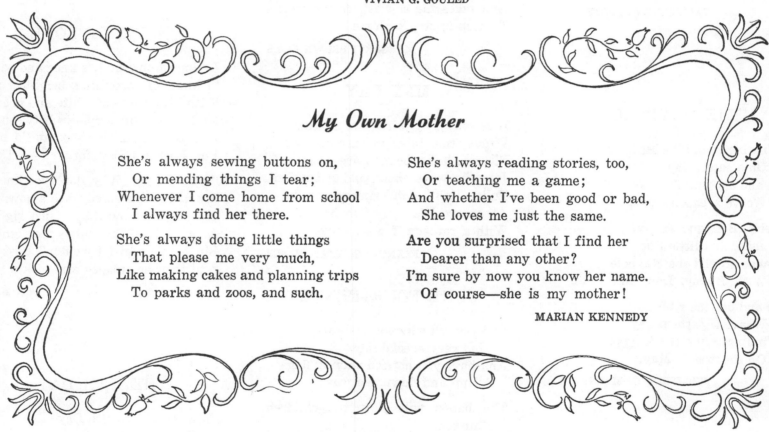

My Own Mother

She's always sewing buttons on,
    Or mending things I tear;
Whenever I come home from school
    I always find her there.

She's always doing little things
    That please me very much,
Like making cakes and planning trips
    To parks and zoos, and such.

She's always reading stories, too,
    Or teaching me a game;
And whether I've been good or bad,
    She loves me just the same.

Are you surprised that I find her
    Dearer than any other?
I'm sure by now you know her name.
    Of course—she is my mother!

MARIAN KENNEDY

ON MOTHER'S DAY

Tomorrow's Mother's special day!
So Betty, Bob, and I
Want her to be happy,
And we are going to try

To be very kind and helpful,
And not to frown or fuss,
So she will know we're grateful
For all she does for us.

We have some lovely flowers
To give to Mother dear;
And we've resolved to make her day
The best in all the year.

WINIFRED C. MARSHALL

A LITTLE MOTHER SPEAKS

I'm going to start my work right
        now!
    I'll hang up Linda's clothes,
I'll sweep and dust my new doll house,
    And mend my Martha's hose.

I'll wash my windows till they shine,
    I'll polish every spoon,
And if there's time, I'll bake a pie,
    For Bobby's lunch, at noon.

I'll brush my baby's shining curls,
    And tuck her in at night—
It makes a difference all one's life,
    If one gets started right.

WINIFRED C. MARSHALL

FLOWERS FOR MOTHER

I never have a special day
    To give flowers to my mother;
I give them to her every day
    To show how much I love her.

When I sweep the kitchen floor,
    Or care for baby brother,
Run on errands, or make the beds,
    I'm giving flowers to Mother.

It's lots of fun pretending
    And to hear my mother say,
"Thank you, dear, for all the flowers
    You've given me today."

CLARA RADER

MEMORIAL DAY

Memorial Day!
Exalted day!
Bringing memorial to all

Of gallant men,
True-hearted men,
Answering their country's call

With this quick cry:
"Here! Here am I,
Ready to stand or fall!"

In thought and deed,
Heroes indeed,
No fears their hearts appall;

And thus today,
Memorial Day,
Our heroes still enthrall!

HARRIETTE W. PORTER

THE MAYPOLE

Winding round the Maypole,
   On a sunny day,
In and out the ribbons
   Weave a pattern gay.

Betty, Bob, and Teddy,
   Jean, and little Sue
Dance around the Maypole,
   With Jimmy, Don, and Prue.

In and out the ribbons
Weave a pattern gay,
Winding round the Maypole,
   On the first of May.

WINIFRED C. MARSHALL

DAY OF MEMORIES

This is a day of memories
Of loyal hearts, and true,
   Of hearts that beat like ours to-day,
Of hearts that loved, of hearts that
      longed
   To live and sing, to work and play.

Now have come years of peace again,
Of lasting peace, we pray.
   Still may we honor in our songs
That loyal band who for our land
   Died, hoping still to right its
      wrongs.

EMMA W. LITTLE

DADDY'S STEPS

When Daddy walks along the street
And hurries home to me,
He takes the quickest, longest steps
That ever I did see.
But when I go to walk with him,
He acts quite diff'rently,
And takes the slowest, shortest ones
To keep in step with me.

MARGARET BROWN ELMS

MAY DAY

It is May Day, birds are singing,
Winds from fairyland are playing,
Blossom-laden boughs are swaying!
Jonquils wave their golden banners,
Tulips light each crimson candle;
All the world's a gay May basket
With a rainbow for a handle.

FRANCES GORMAN RISSER

JUNE FOURTEENTH

Can you tell why we celebrate
   This very special day,
And have you noticed waving flags
   All up and down the way?

The bands will play, the children
      march,
   And all the crowds will cheer.
It is the birthday of our flag,
   A day that we hold dear.

WINIFRED C. MARSHALL

ARBOR DAY

I cannot dig a great big hole
   And set a tree into it,
But I can make a little hole
   And I am going to do it.

Then in the little hole I'll drop
   This acorn brown and shiny,
And that way I can plant a tree
   Although I am so tiny.

ALICE CROWELL HOFFMAN

FATHER'S DAY

On Father's Day I try to see
How happy I can make Dad be;
I try to be just extra good;
And do each small thing as I should.

I'm extra helpful, thoughtful too,
And quick to see things I should do.
Then Dad grins, happy as can be
As he sits there and watches me.

So I think it would be fun
To make *each* day a happy one—
Have Father's Day not once a year,
But every day to hold it dear!

GRAYCE KROGH BOLLER

A TIE OF LOVE

I climbed on Daddy's knee and said,
"I know of something, brightest red,
With little spots of white and green,
And stripes of purple in between,
And if I could, that's what I'd buy
For Father's Day for you—a tie."

"A tie for me? Why, don't you know,"
My daddy answered, face aglow,
"I have one now that is just right—
A tie of love, that binds me tight;
But here's a gift I wouldn't miss."
And then he stooped and took a kiss.

DON MOON

HEALTH DAY

May Day is Health Day
   For children everywhere,
The day to think of healthy things
   Like food and sun and air;

The day to stop to value
   The blessing of good health,
And count it first in measuring
   The things that make for wealth.

A nation's biggest asset
   Is not concerned with gold,
But healthy minds and bodies
   In children, young and old.

So, each who loves his country
   Can strive to do his part
By trying to keep healthy
   In body, mind, and heart.

SOLVEIG PAULSON RUSSELL

POEMS CHILDREN ENJOY

A BOY LIKE ME

I think Christopher Columbus
　　Must have been a boy like me,
When he lived in days long past
　　In the land of Italy.
He must have sat upon the quay
　　And let his feet hang down,
And watched the ships come to and
　　fro
From a far-off Eastern town.

Perhaps he wondered as he sat,
　　And dreamed some great day-
　　dreams,
Of other wharfs where ships were
　　docked
　　And other bright-hued scenes.
Oh, Columbus was a wondrous man,
　　As fine as fine could be;
Yet I think when he was just a boy
　　He must have been like me.

　　　　　　CHARLOTTE SWANEY

A NEW WORLD

Columbus found a new world
　　Because he dared to do
A thing that was unheard of—
　　A thing that was quite new.

Columbus found a new world
　　Because he made a start,
Instead of merely pond'ring o'er
　　The thoughts within his heart.

Columbus found a new world
　　Because he saw things through—
And you can find your new world
　　Precisely that way, too.

　　　　　　ALICE CROWELL HOFFMAN

A SONG OF COLUMBUS

In Genoa's harbor, wide and blue,
　　Columbus as a child
Saw the wondrous caravels
　　That braved high winds and wild.

Pearls and shining ivory,
　　Gold and flaming dyes,
The westbound caravels would bring
　　To charm Italian eyes.

From Genoa they'd eastward go,
　　Laden to the line
With pitch and tar and silken stuffs,
　　Thick woolens and fine wine.

Near and far the ships would go,
　　With sailors brave and strong.
At fourteen he was proud to sail
　　On an outbound ship along.

Year in, year out, to distant ports,
　　Each year he braver grew;
Each year more of the starry sky,
　　More of the sea he knew.

With bravery and knowledge sure,
　　And with a spirit meek,
At last this master sailor dared
　　New ocean ways to seek.

Our land he found, this land we love,
　　Which, though without his name,
Honors him forevermore,
　　Whose faith won him his fame.

　　　　　　NORMAN C. SCHLICHTER

The Three Ships

The Niña, the Pinta, the Santa Maria,
　　Three little ships from Spain,
Sailed over the seas, under skies so
　　blue,
　　Sailed on through the wind and rain.
　　So brave was the captain,
　　So gallant his crew,
　　Their faith remained steadfast
　　Till their goal came in view.
The Niña, the Pinta, the Santa Maria,
　　Three little ships from Spain,
Inspired the later pioneers
　　Who settled on hill and plain.
　　So great was their labor,
　　Their courage so true,
　　That our mighty nation
　　From their striving grew.

　　　　　　LILLIAN W. ALLARD

CHRISTOPHER COLUMBUS

Columbus was a wise man
　　Who thought the earth was round;
He planned to sail across the sea
　　Where trading could be found.

Though kings did not believe in him,
　　And men thought he would fail,
He found one friend, the Spanish
　　queen,
　　Who gave him ships to sail.

The crew rebelled, the sea was rough
　　In 1492;
Still this brave man kept sailing on
　　In spite of sea or crew.

But when they spied America,
　　They landed with a cheer—
And that is why we celebrate
　　Columbus Day each year.

　　　　　　GERTRUDE M. ROBINSON

LIKE COLUMBUS

Columbus said, "The earth is round.
Across the sea I'll go.
Although some say the earth is flat,
I'll prove it is not so."

Columbus crossed the ocean. When
His sailors cried, "Turn back!"
He would not listen to their pleas,
But kept the onward track.

Then when Columbus sighted land,
Their cries and fears were gone.
I hope that I shall be as brave
As he was, and "sail on!"

　　　　　　ELEANOR DENNIS

POMPOUS MR. PUMPKIN

Pompous Mr. Pumpkin,
You needn't look so wise,
Perched upon a picket fence
Staring with your eyes—

Needn't think that I'm afraid
Of your fearful frown
Or your great big glaring teeth
Or your mouth, turned down;

Mr. Pumpkin, run from *you?*
No, sir—no, indeed—
Because I knew you long ago
When you were just a seed!

ELSIE MELCHERT FOWLER

FUNNY FEAR

I don't like people to shout "BOO"
When we are out at play;
I don't like to feel *shivery*
On any other day,
But, somehow, creepy games are *fun;*
I like to think I've seen
A witch or bat, queer things like that,
When it is Halloween!

FRANCES GORMAN RISSER

UNHAPPY PUMPKIN

The pumpkin was unhappy, for
He did not want to stay
Tied to a vine, beneath the corn,
And never go away.

He wished he were the sun, so he
Could roll around the sky.
"If I keep growing like him, I
May get there by and by."

Though he grew big and yellow, he
Was not the sun. Instead
He became a jack-o'-lantern
With a candle in his head.

LOUISA J. BROOKER

PUMPKINS

A farmer grew pumpkins;
So, late in the Fall,
He went out one day
And he gathered them all!

The biggest and roundest
He sent to the fair
In hopes of its winning
A blue ribbon there.

The rest went to market,
Except for a few;
His wife made some pies
Of all except two.

And what of the two?
Oh, they're a surprise
With long, jagged teeth
And a light in their eyes!

NONA KEEN DUFFY

A GOOD DISGUISE

"I'm going to dress myself so queer
For Halloween," I said, "this year,

Nobody else will ever guess
That I am little Mary Bess."

I put my old clothes all in place,
I fastened on my funny face,

Looked in the glass above the shelf,
And didn't even know myself!

ALICE CROWELL HOFFMAN

JACK-O'-LANTERN GARDEN

I wish I had a garden,
Where the warm sun brightly
shines.
I'd plant each nook and corner
With jack-o'-lantern vines.

Then, from my little garden
I'd pick for Halloween
More golden jack-o'-lanterns
Than you have ever seen.

Of course, I'd choose the biggest,
The one that's brightest gold,
To peep in at your window—
Oh, there, I almost told!

GERTRUDE M. ROBINSON

THE JACK-O'-LANTERN

Billy brought a pumpkin in
And Mother scraped it out.
Daddy carved a little mouth
With such a funny pout.

Sally cut some crooked eyes
And trimmed the thing with beads,
While everybody laughed at me
Because I saved the seeds.

But I will plant them in the spring
And wait till fall, and *then* —
I'll have at least a hundred
Jack-o'-lantern men!

FLORENCE LIND

A PUMPKIN SEED

A pumpkin seed's a little thing,
When it is planted in the spring,
But, oh, the fun that it can bring!

At Halloween it turns into
A pumpkin pie for me and you,
Or jack-o'-lantern that says "Boo!"

ALICE CROWELL HOFFMAN

THE PUMPKIN THAT GREW

One time there was a pumpkin,
And all the summer through
It stayed upon a big green vine,
And grew, and grew, and grew!

It grew from being small and green
To being big and yellow
And then it said unto itself,
"Now I'm a handsome fellow!"

And then one day it grew a mouth,
A nose, and two big eyes!
And so that pumpkin grew into
A jack-o'-lantern wise!

M. LUCILLE FORD

HALLOWEEN HELPERS

"Happy Halloween is coming,"
  Said the Spirit of October.
"Who will help to make the people
  Frolicsome instead of sober?"

"I will," said a big black cat.
"I will come and scat, scat, scat,"

"I'll make faces through the night,"
Said a jack-o'-lantern bright.

"Let us help," said all the witches,
"With our broomsticks and our
  switches."

"For your doings I will prowl,"
Hooted then a big-eyed owl.

"I'll be there; you need me most,"
Squeaked the voice of some lone
  ghost.

"We'll be peeping out from nooks,"
Added one of many spooks.

"Right beside him we will roam,"
Said a goblin and a gnome.

"Thank you for your willing offers,"
  Said the Spirit of October.
"Surely now we'll make the people
  Frolicsome instead of sober."

                ALICE CROWELL HOFFMAN

A HALLOWEEN WISH

If I could borrow a witch's broom,
  I'd ride far above the town;
I'd see the place where the sun
    comes up,
  The place where the moon goes
    down.

I'd fly around by the old church tower
  And wave to the folk below;
I'd see the haunts of the wise night
    owl
  And follow the fireflies' glow.

I shouldn't care for a tall black hat
  Or cat with fiery eye—
But I'd like to borrow a magic broom
  And fly as the witches fly.

                MABEL HARMER

TWO YELLOW PUMPKINS

Once there were two yellow pumpkins,
  Growing on a vine;
And they said to one another,
  "Aren't we just fine!
Wonder what to us will happen
  When we go from here,
Will we be turned to chariots golden
  And travel far and near?"

One day there came into the cornfield
  A little girl and boy;
Each one seized a yellow pumpkin,
  As though it were some toy.
Said Boy, "I'll make a jack-o'-lantern,
  Now won't that be great?
His face shall be so big and funny,
  He'll surely be 'first rate.' "

Said she, "I'll bake my yellow
    pumpkin
  Into a pie so nice;
Then let me share your jack-o'-lantern,
  And I'll give you a slice."
And so, that night when all was
    quiet—
  At least for Halloween—
They sat beside the jack-o'-lantern,
  With the golden pie between.
              BLANCHE A. STEINHOVER

HALLOWEEN FUN

Tang of cider in the air,
Spooks and goblins everywhere,
Caldrons bubbling in the night,
Jack-o'-lanterns burning bright
Gypsies stirring steaming brew.
On the fences black cats mew.
Bats in darkened corners hide.
Lurid witches broomsticks ride.
Skulls and crossbones act as hosts
To rows and rows of stately ghosts.
  That's Halloween!

                FERN CURTIS

HALLOWEEN

Brown streaks on the lawn,
  Frost elfins a-prancing,
Brown pods on the flowers,
  Seed fairies a-dancing.

The brownies are climbing
  And painting the trees,
And little ice-pixies
  Are chilling the breeze.

The red squirrel's whisking
  His nut stores away;
The chipmunks are frisking
  Each hour of the day.

By such signs as these
  Let all children remember
Day after to-morrow's
  The first of November.

                CAROLYN R. FREEMAN

HALLOWEEN COSTUMES

The strangest sights you've ever seen
Come to view on Halloween:

Ghosts and tumbling acrobats,
Witches in their pointed hats.

Look at all the things we've made
For our Halloween parade!

See the costumes of the elves!
We designed them all, ourselves.

See the charming fairies dance!
Watch the gypsies gaily prance!

See the brownies with their packs!
All their clothes we made from sacks!

See the goblins strut and caper!
We made their suits from wrapping
    paper!

Bats and owls come swooping by
In the twinkling of an eye.

What a jolly, fine parade,
Showing suits the class has made!

                NONA KEEN DUFFY

Heroes We Never Name

Back of the men we honor
  Enrolled on the scroll of fame,
Are the millions who go unmen-
    tioned—
  The heroes we never name!
Those who have won us the victories,
  And conquered along the way;
Those who have made us a nation—
  A tribute to them I would pay.

Back of our nation's first leader,
  Of Lincoln and Wilson, too,
Back of the mind directing our course
  Was the army that carried it
    through.
Back of the generals and captains
  Was the tramping of rank and file,
And back of them were the ones at
  home
  Who labored with tear and with
    smile.

And what of the "everyday" heroes
  Whose courage and efforts ne'er
    cease!
Toilers who struggle and labor and
  strive
  And hope for a future of peace?
Hats off to the worthy leaders;
  Their honor I'd ever acclaim—
But here's a cheer for the many
  brave,
  The heroes we never name!

                  M. LUCILLE FORD

A THANKSGIVING DINNER

Take a turkey, stuff it fat,
Some of this and some of that.
Get some turnips, peel them well;
Cook a big squash in its shell.

Now potatoes, big and white,
Mash till they are soft and light.
Cranberries, so tart and sweet,
With the turkey we must eat.

Pickles—yes—and then, oh, my!
For dessert a pumpkin pie,
Golden brown and spicy sweet.
What a fine Thanksgiving treat!

            MAUDE M. GRANT

THE TURKEY'S OPINION

"What dost thou think of drumsticks?"
  I asked a barn-yard bird.
He grinned a turkey grin, and then
  He answered me this word:

"They're good to eat, they're good
  to beat;
  But sure as I am living,
They're best to run away with
  The week before Thanksgiving."

            ANNA M. PRATT

VETERANS DAY VISION

I saw a cross upon a hill—
  A cross like some weird lily;

It marked the place a soldier lay—
  It made me creepy, chilly.

I saw a time beyond the cross
  When men no longer would
Wage war on one another—
  A time of brotherhood.

       ALICE CROWELL HOFFMAN

GIVE THANKS

For all the blessings that are ours,
For all our food, for lovely flowers,
  Give thanks!
For trees that give us fruit to eat,
For winter cold and summer heat,
  Give thanks!

For Mother's love and Father's aid,
For all the wonders God has made,
  Give thanks!
For friends and toys with which to
  play,
For restful night, and joyous day,
  Give thanks!

       CARMEN LAGOS SIGNES

A THANKSGIVING RIDE

Five jolly, fat pumpkins one moonlight
  night,
  Said, "Come, let us all take a ride;

The turkeys will take us, with ease
  and delight."
  So they all rode away in great pride.

But soon Mistress Cook cried out in
  dismay,
  "Oh, where are my turkeys and pies?"

"They all went away, to spend Thanksgiving Day,"
  Said the moon, laughing down from
  the skies.

          ELLA M. POWERS

A THANKSGIVING PRAYER

I'm thankful that the world was made
  Big and wide and round,
So that there would be room on it,
  And space could still be found
For all the little children's homes
  To cuddle snugly down
Across the snowy countryside,
  In city and in town.

       ALICE CROWELL HOFFMAN

SIGNS OF THANKSGIVING

There are pies all set away in rows
   Upon the pantry shelf;
And plum pudding in the cake box,
   Alone, all by itself.

There's mincemeat nice and spicy
   Stewing on the kitchen stove;
I know it's full of raisins,
   And cinnamon and clove.

There are pumpkins big and golden,
   Lying out upon the field,
And heaps and heaps of apples,
   All the orchard trees can yield.

There's a tangy, frosty sweetness
   Glowing in the autumn air,
And a kind of happy feeling
   Around 'most everywhere.

Out in the yard our turkey
   Is strutting all around,
Picking up the yellow corn
   That's scattered on the ground.

He doesn't seem to mind one bit,
   Although it's very clear
That he knows what is coming—
   Thanksgiving's almost here!

FRANCES WRIGHT TURNER

THE PINE-CONE TURKEY

Once a little pine-cone turkey,
   With feathers stiff and hard,
Wished that he could gobble loudly
   Like turkeys in the yard.
They gobbled high, they gobbled low,
   They gobbled with a trill;
And the little pine-cone turkey
   Could only keep quite still.

But when he stood on the table
   On last Thanksgiving Day,
And saw a big brown turkey there
   His heart was light and gay.
His heart sang high, his heart sang
     low,
   His heart sang with a trill;
And the little pine-cone turkey
   Was glad he'd kept quite still!

MABEL MAURINE HENDERSON

A THANKSGIVING FABLE

It was a hungry pussy cat, upon
   Thanksgiving morn,
And she watched a thankful little
   mouse, that ate an ear of corn.
"If I ate that thankful little mouse,
   how thankful he should be,
When he had made a meal himself, to
   make a meal for me!
Then with his thanks for having fed,
   and thanks for feeding me,
With all *his* thankfulness inside, how
   thankful I shall be!"
Thus mused the hungry pussy cat,
   upon Thanksgiving Day;
But the little mouse had overheard
   and declined (with thanks) to
   stay.

OLIVER HERFORD

The Mayflower

Across Atlantic waters drear,
Defiant of the winds that roar,

Through heavy seas it dared to steer
A fearless course to freedom's shore.

More precious than rare gems or gold,
Across the ocean's billowy foam

In safety came, deep in the hold,
The daily needs of hearth and home.

The tilting decks were bravely trod
By heroes of a faith sublime,

Who asked in daily prayers to God
For freedom in a foreign clime.

Throughout our nation's history,
This fearless ship will ever stand

A symbol of democracy,
A tribute to our Pilgrim band.

LELAND B. JACOBS

HOLIDAYS THROUGH THE YEAR

GRATITUDE

I have a box
Full of all kinds of blocks,
And a little toy wagon painted red;
And a ball to roll
And a bread-and-milk bowl,
And a soft pink blanket for my bed.

I have a silver spoon
And a purple balloon
And boots, when the rain rains hard;
And a Daddy and a Mommie
And a big brother Tommie,
And a sand pile in my yard—

Don't you think a child like me
Should very, very thankful be?

JOSEPHINE VAN DOLZEN PEASE

WE ARE THANKFUL

For all good things to do
And see upon the earth,
For all things old and new
That fill the days with worth,
For all the joys that leaven
The busy lives we live,
For friends and home and heaven,
Our thanks to God we give.

CLAUDE WEIMER

A CHILD'S SONG

I'm thankful for the sunshine bright,
For rain and for stars at night;
I'm thankful for each flower and tree,
And all the beauty that I see.

I'm grateful for our singing birds
And for my mother's gentle words;
I'm grateful for kind friends and
true;
Help me to be a good friend, too.

ALICE F. GREEN

DAILY THANKS

Everything on Grandpa's farm
Makes known its gratitude
By giving, in some simple way,
Its thanks for daily food.

When Grandpa feeds the chicks and
hens,
They gather round his feet,
And cluck to say they're thankful for
The grain they have to eat.

The horses whinny when they're fed,
Which is their way to say
Their thanks for pails of golden oats
And mangers of sweet hay.

If animals can find a way
To show their gratitude
I'll not forget to say a prayer
Of thanks for daily food.

EUNICE CASSIDY HENDRYX

A THANKSGIVING HYMN

The Lord hath done great things for
us,
Whereof we are glad.
Oh, may our voices praises sing
For blessings we have had!
For days of peace and happiness,
For health and strength and cheer,
We thank thee, God of heaven and
earth,
And hold thy mem'ry dear.

The Lord hath done great things for
us,
Oh, may we ever sing
True songs of loving gratitude,
And happy praises bring!
The year with goodness he hath
crowned,
His mercies hath shown clear;
We thank thee, God of heaven and
earth,
And hold thy mem'ry dear.

M. LUCILLE FORD

GLAD THANKSGIVING DAY

November days are cheerful
Though frost is in the air,
For it's then that Nature gives us
Her gifts for all to share.

Her gifts for all to share,
And so we store away,
But best of all we love it
For glad Thanksgiving Day.

The golden corn is gathered,
The bins are running o'er,
The cellar's full to bursting
With such a goodly store.

With such a goodly store,
All treasured there it lay,
And so we praise the Giver
For glad Thanksgiving Day.

EFFIE CRAWFORD

FOR COMMON JOYS

Thanksgiving for each joyful song
We hear along the way,
For voices that are dear to us,
The birds' glad roundelay.

Thanksgiving for each beauty new
That greets our seeking eyes;
For the sunset's glow and the day's
full cheer,
And every dawn's surprise.

Thanksgiving for the boundless love
That surges in on every side;
For blessings from the hand of God
And for the good that they provide.

Thanksgiving for each precious gift
Life brings and bids us treasure;
For common joys of every day,
For good things without measure
Let us give thanks!

M. LUCILLE FORD

THE CHRISTMAS STAR

A star is on our Christmas tree.
  Do you know why it's there?
It happened many years ago,
  Upon a night quite fair,
That shepherds, biding in the fields,
  Were wakened from their sleep,
And watched a lovely, shining star
  Across the heavens creep.

They followed it until it stopped
  Above a stable door.
They tiptoed in and saw a Babe,
  Then followed it no more.
For Jesus in that manger slept,
  A star had shown the way.
That's why a star is on our tree
  On every Christmas Day.

ALICE M. JAROS

THE FIRST CHRISTMAS

The shepherds watched their flocks by
    night,
When suddenly there came a light
Which brightened all the evening sky,
And those who saw it wondered why.

To Bethlehem they traveled far,
Guided by that wondrous star,
For there in manger calm and mild
Lay the Christ, the Holy Child.

Wise men saw, and followed, too,
Bearing gifts of wondrous hue
To place before their Lord and King;
Treasures rare each wished to bring.

And so today we gather here
To sing our songs both loud and clear,
And bring the tidings once again,
"Peace on earth, good will to men."

ANSTRICE CARTER KELLOGG

The stars came out to shine that
    night,
They twinkled and shone so very
    bright—
The night that Christ was born.
The angels sang from heaven high,
Their songs resounding through the
    sky—
The night that Christ was born.

The shepherds watched their lambs
    and sheep,
And flocks were wrapped in peaceful
    sleep—
The night that Christ was born.
The Bethlehem star was bright that
    night,
Three Wise Men traveled by its
    light—
The night that Christ was born.

They carried wondrous gifts, we're
    told,
Of frankincense and myrrh and
    gold—
The night that Christ was born.
They traveled to the manger bed,
And there in prayer each bowed his
    head—
The night that Christ was born.

And so together heaven and earth
Were filled with joy at the Christ
    Child's birth—
The night that Christ was born.

RUTH COX

CAROLS

Carols are such pretty things
'Specially when my mother sings,
  "Silent night, holy night,
  All is calm, all is bright."

She turns the lights so low and dim
Before she croons this Christmas
    hymn,
  "Round yon virgin mother and
    Child!
  Holy Infant, so tender and mild."

I cuddle close in Mother's arm
I know she'll keep me from all harm.
  "Sleep in heavenly peace,
  Sleep in heavenly peace."

Carols are such pretty things,
I seem to hear the angels' wings.
Before she croons this Christmas hymn,
  "Round yon virgin mother and Child!"

SARAH LITCHFIELD

CRADLE HYMN

Away in a manger, no crib for a bed,
The little Lord Jesus laid down his
    sweet head.
The stars in the bright sky looked
    down where he lay—
The little Lord Jesus asleep on the
    hay.

The cattle are lowing, the baby
    awakes,
But little Lord Jesus no crying he
    makes.
I love thee, Lord Jesus! Look down
    from the sky,
And stay by my cradle till morning
    is nigh.

MARTIN LUTHER

WHAT THIS COUNTRY NEEDS

The house is full of packages,
  Mysterious and gay,
But everyone is labeled
  In the meanest sort of way.

"Do Not Open until Christmas!"
  'Most every label reads;
So I've come to the conclusion
  That what this country needs

Is someone to manufacture
  Some labels plain and bright:
"Open This Package when You
  Please."
Now, don't you think I'm right?

INEZ GEORGE GRIDLEY

BABY'S STOCKING

Our baby's stocking is so small
  I'm 'fraid when Santa comes,
It won't hold many pretty toys
  Or nuts or sugar plums.

I think when no one's looking,
  I'll just creep down the stair,
And take down Baby's tiny sock,
  And hang a long one there.

WINIFRED C. MARSHALL

THE CHRISTMAS STOCKING

My stocking's full of Christmas things,
A train that runs, a top that sings,
A tooting horn, a candy cane,
A green and shining toy airplane.

And oh, it is such Christmas fun
To find each treasure, one by one,
And last of all, the best, I know,
The big red apple in the toe!

JOSEPHINE VAN DOLZEN PEASE

A GOOD EXAMPLE

The folks that live in Sweden
  To poles tie sheaves of wheat
So that the birds on Christmas
  Shall have enough to eat.

We cannot go to Sweden,
  But we can do as they
And give our friends, the bird folk,
  A feast on Christmas Day.

ALICE CROWELL HOFFMAN

A TRIP TO TOWN

We went to town the other day,
To look for Santa with his sleigh.
And, sure enough, we found him there
With suit of red, and snowy hair.

He shook my hand and laughed with
  glee
And took me then upon his knee.
He seemed so big and jolly, too;
I love old Santa Claus, don't you?

ANSTRICE CARTER KELLOGG

SANTA UP-TO-DATE

My grandma tells how Santa Claus
  drove eight or ten reindeer,
And if you'd listen in the night,
  the sound of bells you'd hear;
Then, with his sleigh piled up so high
  you couldn't see the top,
He'd make his round of visits and
  no home was e'er forgot,
    In days of long ago.

Well, maybe reindeer were all right
  in days of long ago,
But in this day of "hurry-up" a
  reindeer is too slow.
So Santa has decided he will be up-
  to-date
And run no risks with reindeer that
  might get him 'round too late—
    So he flies an airship now.

If ever I can see his airplane in the
  sky,
You bet I'll have my dad fix a good
  landing place close by.
So 'stead of bells a-ringing, if you
  listen in the night,
You'll hear his motor roaring, and
  you'll know he's come all right—
    For he drives an airship

ADA ROSE DEMEREST

MOTHER'S CHRISTMAS

It's just ten days until Christmas
  and so
I've counted my pennies and made
  plans to go
To the best of the shops—something
  special, you know—
To select a fine gift for my mother!

I wonder how much of my money
  'twill take—
If any's left over, I'll buy her a cake
With the very best icing the baker
  can make—
What a Christmas I'll make for my
  mother!

SARAH GRAMES CLARK

SHOPPING EARLY

I'll do my shopping early,
  This year at Christmas time.
I've saved my birthday dollar,
  Some pennies, and a dime.

I have my list of presents
  All written out, you see.
Tomorrow I'll go shopping,
  And Jean will go with me.

It will be very pleasant,
  When Christmas Day draws near,
To know I need not hurry,
  The way I did last year.

WINIFRED C. MARSHALL

CHRISTMAS

The time draws near the birth of
  Christ;
  The moon is hid; the night is still;
  The Christmas bells from hill to hill
Answer each other in the mist.

Four voices of four hamlets round,
  From far and near, on mead and
    moor,
  Swell out and fail, as if a door
Were shut between me and the sound:

Each voice four changes on the wind,
  That now dilate, and now decrease,
  Peace and goodwill, goodwill and
    peace,
Peace and goodwill, to all mankind.

ALFRED, LORD TENNYSON

POEMS CHILDREN ENJOY

CHRISTMAS EVE

The mantel clock's ticking so slow,
  so slow;
The stockings are waiting all hung
  in a row;
From biggest to smallest so limply
  they wait,
Hoping for filling before it is late.

They look so expectant; they haven't
  a doubt,
And mysterious secrets are flying
  about;
What can it be to excite each one so?
Oh, surely you don't mean that you
  do not know?

With stockings just waiting so
  patiently there,
And secrets galore floating up every
  stair?
They're waiting to see what good
  Santa will leave,
For tonight stars are bright—it is
  now Christmas Eve!

GRAYCE KROGH BOLLER

GOOD-BY, TOYLAND

The jumping jacks and Teddy bears,
  And dolls both large and small
Have all been packed in Santa's sleigh,
  And now they gaily call,
"Good-by to Santa's workshop
  And Santa's busy crew;
Good-by, good-by to toyland,
  And Mrs. Santa too.
We're ready, jolly Santa Claus,
  Please take us on our way
To make the children happy
  On Christmas Day."

LELAND B. JACOBS

SANTA AT WORK

Christmas Eve was drawing near,
  And there was much to do,
Though Santa Claus had worked all
  year
  In order to be through.

The sleigh stood ready by the shop,
  The reindeer in their stable,
And Santa Claus worked very fast—
  As fast as he was able.

He painted rosy cheeks on dolls
  And glued their wigs on tight;
He painted all the croquet balls
  And made them gay and bright.

Skis and skates and shiny sleds
  Were piled upon the floor
With building blocks and dollies' beds
  And other toys galore.

Now Christmas Eve had come at last
  The Christmas stars were bright,
And Santa hitched his reindeer fast
  To the sleigh in the frosty night.

Then into the sleigh he packed his
  load
  Of wonderful dolls and toys,
And with a shake of the reins he rode
  away
  With his gifts for girls and boys.

RUTH COX

A CHRISTMAS BIRTHDAY

This is my dear little Elizabeth Rose!
I got her last Christmas, as you might
  suppose.
Dear Santa put her on my Christmas
  tree,
I know that he made her just special
  for me!

She's been such a comfort to me all
  the year,
Not once she's been naughty, or let
  fall a tear!
She goes off to bed like a good child
  should,
And has always behaved just as well
  as she could.

So this is her birthday, and I brought
  her to see
All the wonderful things on the
  Christmas tree;
And I hope that among all these pres-
  ents so fine,
There'll be some little gift for this
  good child of mine!

LEETA McCULLY CHERRY

A CHRISTMAS WISH

I wish old Santa'd bring a sled
With runners that are painted red,

For then I'd play out in the snow
And down the hill I'd swiftly go.

I'd bring the bundles from the store
And leave them at the kitchen door.

I'd be as happy as could be
If Santa'd bring that sled to me.

ANSTRICE CARTER KELLOGG

CHRISTMAS BELLS

Hark! the Christmas bells are ring-
  ing—
  Ringing through the frosty air—
Happiness to each one bringing,
  And release from toil and care.

How the merry peal is swelling
  From the gray old crumbling tower,
To the simplest creature telling
  Of Almighty love and power.

Ankle-deep the snow is lying,
  Every spray is clothed in white,
Yet abroad the folk are hieing,
  Brisk and busy, gay and light.

Now fresh helps and aid are offered
  To the agéd and the poor,
And rare love exchanges proffered
  At the lowliest cottage door.

Neighbors shaking hands and greet-
  ing,
  No one sorrowing, no one sad,
Children, loving parents meeting,
  Young and old alike are glad.

Then while Christmas bells are ring-
  ing,
  Rich and poor, your voices raise,
And—your simple carol singing—
  Waft to heaven your grateful
  praise.

ANONYMOUS

HOLLY AND MISTLETOE

Holly and mistletoe,
  Candles and bells,
I know the message
  That each of you tells.

Ornament, tinsel, and
  Striped candy cane,
What you're suggesting
  Is perfectly plain.

Though you are silent,
  It's really quite clear
That you all are telling me
  Christmas is here.

LELAND B. JACOBS

SNOW FOR CHRISTMAS

Oh, the North Wind told a Snowbird,
  And the Snowbird told the Sun
That 'twas almost time for Christmas—
  Christmas work had best be done!

So the Snowbird, all a-twitter,
  Made some plans for what was best,
And he flew to tell the Snowflakes
  To be up and neatly dressed.

Then the Snowflakes told a Mountain,
  And the Mountain told a Cloud
That 'twas almost time for Christmas—
  No mistakes could be allowed!

And the Cloud, with gay rejoicing,
  Gathered all the Snowflakes white,
And kept them fresh and dainty
  For delivery in the night.

Then the Dream Man told a Dream Sprite,
  And the Dream Sprite told a child
That 'twould be a snowy Christmas—
  In his dream the baby smiled;

But when dawned the Christmas morning
  That big Cloud had slipped away,
And no one even wondered
  Why it snowed for Christmas Day.

SARAH GRAMES CLARK

A SECRET

Do you know why the pine trees
  Stand so straight and tall,
Spread their branches thick and fine,
  And never stoop at all?

It really is a secret
  Which the North Wind told to me:
Every pine tree hopes some day
  To be a Christmas tree.

LAURA ALICE BOYD

DOLLY'S CHRISTMAS TREE

I have been busy all day long,
  Trimming my dolly's tree.
I want it to look like the one
  That Mother trims for me.

I have a box of ornaments
  And all these toys, you see.
It's fun to play I'm Santa Claus,
  And trim my dolly's tree.

WINIFRED C. MARSHALL

CHRISTMAS MAGIC

What a shining
  And Christmasy sight
Of hurrying crowds,
  And of windows alight!

Something of Christmas
  In everyday places,
Something of Christmas
  On all people's faces!

And on the corner,
  A Christmas-tree store
Where only the grocer's
  Was before!

J. VAN DOLZEN PEASE

A CHRISTMAS TREE

The
pine tree that
grew on the hill has
blossomed this morning for
Jack and for Jill. It has blossomed
with lights and gay colored balls, with
cookies and bonbons and whistles and dolls.
The   children
smile brightly-
and then Jack
said   to   Jill,
"It's our little pine tree
That grew on the hill."

WINIFRED C. MARSHALL

MY FAVORITE TREE

Last March I truly thought I loved
  The willow tree the best,
For every tiny little twig
  In soft gray fur was dressed;
But when in May the apple tree
  Was gowned in pink and white,
I felt that nowhere in the world
  Could be a lovelier sight.

Then in July the sun shone hot,
  And our big maple tree
Spread such a deep cool shade about,
  It seemed the best to me.
And yet when I went nutting
  With the girls and boys this fall,
I quite decided that I loved
  The beech tree most of all!

But now that winter time is here
  With all its ice and snow,
I've had to change my mind again;
  At last I'm sure I know
The tree I really love the best;
  And you will all agree
There can be nothing nicer
  Than a shining Christmas tree!

DORIS WHEELER BLOUNT

BUSY

Busy making popcorn balls,
  Busy with the tree,
Busy mailing greeting cards,
  Busy, busy me!

Busy wrapping packages;
  Say, I will be bound—
I'm so busy—I don't see
  How Santa gets around!

LELAND B. JACOBS

WHAT THEN?

If Santa comes, and I'm not asleep,
  What then?
Suppose I took a wee little peep,
  What then?
If he's so jolly as I've been taught,
He shouldn't mind if he did get
  caught.
If he should see me—oh, what a
  thought!
What then?

MABEL F. HILL

Having Fun

THE CIRCUS

The circus came to our town!
   There was a grand parade!
I held on tight to Daddy's hand,
   I was *almost* afraid!

The lions looked like great big cats
   In their cage with golden bars;
A lady rode a barebacked horse,
   Her dress all bright with stars.

The elephants were very large—
   They nearly shook the ground!
And oh, the steam piano made
   A loud and merry sound!

MYRTLE G. BURGER

THE VEGETABLES' CIRCUS

The Turnip turned himself into
  A white and purple top;
He spun and spun *and spun* until
  I thought he'd never stop!

The String Beans danced a tango—
  The way those Beans could bend!
The Onion played at tragedy
  And shed tears without end.

The Spinach and the Lettuce
  In ballet skirts were seen;
The first wore ruffled emerald,
  The other silver green.

The Squash and the Tomato clowned
  And told each other jokes,
While Messrs. Corn and Carrot
  Waltzed with the Artichokes.

The Cabbages played audience
  And sat in stolid rows,
Wept at the actors' funny pranks
  And laughed at all their woes!

MARION DOYLE

THE CIRCUS

Round and round the elephants plod,
The monkeys swing on a shining rod,
Bespangled ponies cavort and prance,
Roly-poly bears do a clumsy dance.
A peddler lifts up his voice to sell
Fresh roasted peanuts in the shell.
The acrobats whirl and loop the loop,
A dog jumps through a flaming hoop.
The circus is a sawdust flower
That blooms for an enchanting hour!

JUNE GRIFFIN WROBLESKI

OUR CIRCUS

Our circus is beginning now—
  That curly dog is Dick's;
The spotted pony is the one
  He rides for clever tricks.
The funny little polar bear
  Is really Baby Sue;
Though polar bears are timid,
  This one will wave at you.
The clown in suit of red and green
  Is quite well trained, you see—
Just watch him walk upon his hands;
  His name is Jimmy Lee.
The circus gave a big parade
  At one o'clock today.
Soon some ice cream we will buy
  With pennies that you pay!

WINIFRED C. MARSHALL

PLAYING CIRCUS

Old Shep made the dandiest camel
  (we tied a hump on his back),
While Patty and Mary rode horses
  (they pranced along down the
    track),
And the cat was a Bengal tiger!
  (we had to pretend he was wild,
For Mouser just wouldn't play circus.
  He went purring along, meek and
    mild.)

Johnny Blake and I were an elephant
  first; then he was a funny clown
And I was the circus man with a whip
  who keeps cracking it up and
  down.
When we marched around past the
  window and Mother saw our
  parade,
She came out with a platter of cookies
  and a pitcher of pink lemonade.

INEZ GEORGE GRIDLEY

THE FAIR

Last year my largest pumpkin
Won first prize at the fair.
This year I'll send a melon
That I've tended with great care;
And Mother has been teaching
Our Betty how to bake—
She's going to send some muffins
And a chocolate layer cake.
It's always so exciting,
Starting to the fair,
To know perhaps your entry
May win a first prize there.

WINIFRED C. MARSHALL

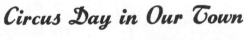

Circus Day in Our Town

At eight o'clock I went to see
The big top rising steadily.
The circus workmen, tanned and
  strong,
Made light their work with joke and
  song,
Till stood the tent, a splendid sight
Of poles and ropes and canvas white.

At ten o'clock the music played,
And down the street the long parade
Swung into view with blast and blare,
With elephant and dancing bear,
With clowns and all the circus joys
That thrill so many girls and boys.

At two o'clock in spirit gay
I saw the circus in full sway.
The lions roared, the ponies pranced,
The tightrope walkers turned and
  danced.
I clapped my hands and had to laugh
To see the clown and the giraffe.

Now when it's time to go to bed
The circus magic fills my head.
I still can hear the music played
And see the rings and the parade.
All night in dreams I hope I see
Each splendid circus memory.

LELAND B. JACOBS

CIRCUS

The brass band blares,
The naphtha flares,
The sawdust smells,
Showmen ring bells,

And oh! right into the circus
    ring
Comes such a lovely, lovely
    thing,
A milk white pony with fly-
    ing tress,
And a beautiful lady,
A beautiful lady,
A beautiful lady in a pink dress!
A red-and-white clown
For joy tumbles down,
Like a pink rose
Round she goes
On her tip-toes
With the pony under—
And then, oh, wonder!
The pony his milk-white tresses
    droops,
And the beautiful lady,
The beautiful lady,
Flies like a bird through the paper
    hoops!

Then he waggles his feet and stands
    on his head,
And the little boys on the twopenny
    seats
Scream with laughter and suck their
    sweets.

                    ELEANOR FARJEON

*From JOAN'S DOOR by Eleanor Farjeon. Copyright, 1926,
by Eleanor Farjeon. Published by J. B. Lippincott Company.*

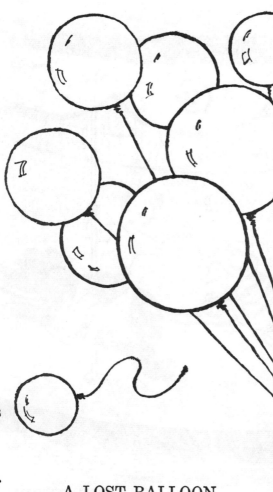

A LOST BALLOON

Tonight, if you notice
    A small, small moon,
I know it will be
    My silver balloon.

I bought one today
    At a circus stand,
And all of a sudden
    It slipped from my hand.

        It will look lovely
        Tonight, but, oh!
        If you know how to get it,
        Please let me know!

                    ELAINE V. EMANS

BUYING BALLOONS

Here comes the man
    Who sells balloons.
Some are as big
    And round as moons.
Red and yellow,
    And green and blue,
Purple, orange,
    And silver, too.
Get your pennies;
    We'll each buy one.
I'll take the red.
    Oh! it's such fun!
Blue and yellow
    And silver moons.
Here comes the man
    Who sells balloons.

                    WINIFRED C. MARSHALL

THE CIRCUS PARADE

I like to hear the patter of the circus
    horses' feet,
As they come prancing gaily down
    the middle of the street.

I wish that I could dress in red and
    on a pony ride
With a plume upon my hat and bright
    buttons down my side.

I'd sit just like a queen and straight
    ahead I'd stare
At the pretty gilded cages of the tiger
    and the bear.

But every now and then I would bow
    my head, to greet
The great crowds of people that lined
    the busy street.

                    ROSE LEARY LOVE

SIMPLE SIMON

Simple Simon met a pieman
    Going to the fair;

Says Simple Simon to the pieman,
    "Let me taste your ware."

Says the pieman to Simple Simon,
    "Show me first your penny";

Says Simple Simon to the pieman,
    "Indeed I have not any."

                    MOTHER GOOSE

MY CHOICE

I like the blowing banners
    That tower toward the sky;
I like the prancing ponies
    With their heads held high.

I like the dancing elephants,
    And bears, both black and brown;
But best of all I think I like
    The jolly circus clown.

He walks, he rides, he slips, he slides,
    He tumbles on his nose,
And merry shouts of laughter rise
    No matter where he goes.

When Father says that I shall be
    A lawyer of renown,
I smile and say, "I'd rather be
    The jolly circus clown."

                    LELAND B. JACOBS

THE MERRY-GO-ROUND

Oh, the merry-go-round, the merry-
go-round;
Its horses never touch the ground!
The music starts and away we go;
Our hats and hair and dresses blow!

Faster and faster on we ride;
We wave to the folks who stand out-
side.
Then all at once the music is slow,
And off the horses we have to go!

FRANCES ARNOLD GREENWOOD

A JOLLY RIDE

The merry-go-round has come to
town;
Let's go for a jolly ride.

Here is the little gilded coach;
Baby Betty can sit inside.

Bobby can ride on a tall giraffe,
And Ted on a tiger, bold.

Martha and Sue like ponies best,
With the bridles of red and gold.

Round and around and around we go,
To the merry jingling tune.

Nothing is ever quite such fun,
As a merry-go-round in June.

WINIFRED C. MARSHALL

MERRY-GO-ROUND

The rollicking, frolicking merry-go-
round
Goes around and around and around,
And the tinkly, twinkly music plays
With a gay and a silvery sound.
The ponies kick their frisky heels
At the tinkly, twinkly sound,
As the rollicking, frolicking merry-
go-round
Goes around and around and around.

If I had my choice each summer day
Of the spot where I'd like to be,
The rollicking, frolicking merry-go-
round
Would be the place for me.
And all of the time that the music
played
With its tinkly, twinkly sound,
I'd go riding around and around,
On the rollicking, frolicking merry-
go-round.

MARIAN KENNEDY

THE FERRIS WHEEL

Here's a delight with which none can
compare,
The sky-riding wheel you see at the
fair!

Over the treetops it carries you high,
Higher and higher, up into the sky—
Then it comes down in the flash of an
eye!

What a delight to turn round and
around,
As high as the roof and then low as
the ground.

Turning and turning it reaches the
top;
Down, down again to the ground it
will drop!
Oh, how I wish that it never would
stop!

JOSEPHINE VAN DOLZEN PEASE

Thoughts to Live By

BRAVERY

Bravery is to face the task
That each passing day may ask;
With strong hearts and purpose true,
We do our best to see things through.

Bravery seeks each foe to face
With a kind and gentle grace
That may win him as a friend,
To prove love conquers in the end.

Bravery looks at every wrong
With conviction firm and strong.
Wrongs, if faced in honest light,
Can be ended and made right.

Bravery clings through doubt or pain
To the thought, "There's much to
    gain;
Every struggle, short or longer,
Won at last, will make me stronger."

M. LUCILLE FORD

Ruth Karbs

FRIENDSHIP'S RULE

Our teacher says there is a rule
We should remember while at school,

At home, at play, whate'er we do,
And that's the rule of friendship true.

If you would have friends, you must
    do
To them the kindly things that you

Would like to have them do and say
To you while at your work and play.

And that's the rule of friendship true;
It works in all we say and do.

It pays to be a friend polite,
For friendship's rule is always right.

                    M. LUCILLE FORD

A GOOD PLAN

My friend, Betty Jo, is very polite;
She *always* does everything kind and right;

She never forgets to say "Thank You," or
    "Please";
And excuses herself with the greatest of
    ease.

She knows just how every person to greet,
Whenever she meets them upon the street.

And everyone likes her because, you see,
She's as kind and pleasant as she can be.

I asked her once, "How do you know
Just what to say or where to go?"

"Oh, I practice at home!" she replied with
    a glance;
"And everywhere else that offers a chance!"

                    M. LUCILLE FORD

LOOKING AHEAD

I look into the glass and see
The little fellow that is me.

He doesn't grow so very fast,
But yet this month he stretches up
    past

The mark where, just two months be-
    fore,
He measured on the cupboard door!

And Mother said, "You're growing,
    Son!
You'll soon be big as anyone."

And then she whispered, "Look away
Toward the man that you will be some
    day!

Look to the future; try to see
The kind of man you want to be.

"The way this little fellow grows
Will make the man the future knows.

So keep him straight and true and
    strong
And clean. You won't have long

To make this little boy you see
Into the man *you* want to be!"

                    M. LUCILLE FORD

GOOD DEEDS

Little acts of friendliness
And ways of being kind
Come out on the rainy days

As if they did not mind
The wet a bit—
In fact as if they're liking it.

"Won't you share my umbrella?"
"May I hold your coat for you?"

"I have my boots on, Mother;
Are there errands I can do?"

                    LUCRETIA PENNY

EFFORT

There's something in a task well done
    That cannot be explained;

A singsong in your heart all day,
    From some fine goal attained.

So is it not worth while for you
    To work with all your might

On any task that you should do,
    And see that it's done right?

For I am sure that you will find,
    When once you have begun,

That honest effort brings success,
    And with it work well done.

                    ESTHER LEE CARTER

JUST A PENNY

I had but a penny—
It looked very small
Not much could I buy with it,
Not much at all.

I looked and I wondered,
I planned and I thought—
What could be done with it?
What could be bought?

The storekeeper asked me,
"Would you like to know
Something you could do
So your penny would grow?"

I knew 'twas not planting
The penny itself.
Then the storekeeper took
A few seeds from his shelf.

"Plant these and then bring me
The pumpkins to sell.
Your penny will grow," he said,
"That I know well."

A dozen fine fruits
On the vines did appear,
And my penny grew up
To a dollar that year!

                    M. LUCILLE FORD

Do Your Best

Do the very best you can,
    Never be a "halfway man";

Even though the task is light,
    Work at it with all your might.

Every hour throughout the day,
    Do you best in every way;

When you have a task to do,
    Never fail to see it through.

                    ESTHER LEE CARTER

Watchword

Two little words   Are pitfalls for
Called "if" and "when"   The best of men.

ESTHER LEE CARTER

THE LOST SMILES

A flock of smiles was lost one day
And couldn't find a place
To rest, because such ugly frowns
Sat on each passing face!

The smiles dropped down upon a tree.
At once the blossoms gay
Began to open on each branch,
In such a happy way

That sight of so much loveliness
Chased frowns from sullen faces;
Then homeless smiles flew down at
    once,
And quickly took their places!

FRANCES GORMAN RISSER

MORNING PRAYER

Our Father, God in Heaven,
  In this our morning prayer,
We give Thee thanks, our Father,
  For all Thy love and care;

For home and friends we thank Thee;
  For music, birds, and flowers;
For winter's snow and lamplight
  For summer's sun and showers.

Help us to grow more gentle,
  More patient, brave, and true;
And may we strive to please Thee
  In all we say and do.

Bless all Thy children, Father,
  Wherever they may be,
In beautiful America.
  Or far across the sea.

MARY HESTER BEAM

A HAPPY YEAR

If we would act toward other folk
  As we would have them do—

Just think how great the happiness
  We'd share the whole year through!

If only thoughts of truthfulness
  And words of loving cheer

Escaped our lips, what happiness
  Would visit us each year!

If we ourselves would promise
  To act from motives true,

Each year would be a happy one
  In everything we do.

M. LUCILLE FORD

THE GAME'S THE THING

Play the game for all you're worth;
Win or lose is not the test,
For we know there's nothing lost
When a man has done his best.

LEAH GIBBS KNOBBE

THE GOOD ATHLETE

The good athlete will sometimes win,
  And sometimes will be losing;
But he will win without a boast,
  And lose without excusing.

ALICE CROWELL HOFFMAN

Freddie Wins a Battle

Old Trouble was a bogeyman
On the hill of "I Don't Care,"

And Freddie was a little boy
Who had no time to spare.

Old Trouble made the lessons hard
And dry as bones, until—

Poor Freddie couldn't see his books
For the bogey on the hill.

He said, "I can't do this at all.
It's just too hard for me."

And, do you know, Old Trouble laughed
And clapped his hands in glee?

Fred said again, "It's just too hard,
No use to even try."

And then he laid his pencil down,
And started in to cry.

And Old Man Trouble grew and grew
In his house upon the hill,

And got so strong and big and bold
And impudent, until—

Young Freddie picked his pencil up
And said, "I'll get to work

And give the thing a whirl, at least!
I'm really not a shirk."

Old Trouble shrank and shrank and shrank
Until he got so small

That soon there wasn't any hill
Or bogeyman at all!

Young Freddie got his work all done
And scampered out to play—

And never since has Trouble come
To ruin Freddie's day.

RACHEL M. ROLSHEIM

TRYING

With a smile on your lips and a
light in your eye,
When asked to do something,
say, "All right, I'll try!"
Then with purpose set high and
the will to go through it,
Though the task may be hard, you
will find you can do it!

M. LUCILLE FORD

HOW TO WORK

If you're asked to do a task,
Start right in to do it;

Willingness will lighten work
And soon you will be through it.

Perhaps to whistle or to sing
A favorite song will cheer you,

And cheerfulness makes light of
work
And comforts others near you.

M. LUCILLE FORD

TWO FAIRIES

There are two lovely fairies
Who make us feel at ease;
Here are the names they're known
by:
"Thank you!" and "If you please!"
They make our life more pleas-
ant,
As everyone agrees;
Those two most welcome fairies:
"Thank you!" and "If you please!"
In fact, I know you'll never
Find a truer friend than these
Soft-spoken, kindly fairies:
"Thank you!" and "If you please!"

CLARENCE M. LINDSAY

LET IT GROW

When you have a happy thought,
  Be careful not to hide it,
Because the thing for you to do,
If you are kind and sweet and true—
And I am saying this to YOU—
  Is, right away, divide it!
A happy thought is something fine
  That grows to be a treasure,
But only if you give a part,
With generous and joyous heart,
To someone—then you've made a start
  To bring it to full measure.
The one to whom you give a share
  Will in delight receive it;
He will divide it with a friend,
And think how far it will extend—
Some say that it will never end,
  And I—oh, I believe it!

EVANTHA CALDWELL

THE FAITHFUL CLOCK

My mother's little ivory clock
  Ticks softly, surely, all day long;
It never hurries, never lags,
  But always sings its rhythmic song.

It tells me when to go to school
  And when it's time for work or
  play;
Its slender hands move endlessly
  To show the proper time of day.

I want to be dependable;
  I'll try my very best to be
As true and helpful to my friends
  As Mother's clock has been to me.

BLOSSOM BENNETT

MY HOBBY HORSE

I have a little hobbyhorse
  Whose name is Silly Pride.

He takes me up, he takes me down
  When we go out to ride.

He never takes me anywhere
  I really ought to go,

And so just what to do with him
  I'm sure I do not know.

I cannot use or give away
  Or sell a silly horse,

And so I must just conquer him,
  And let him know I'm boss.

MONICA WILLIAMS

Never Say Fail!

Keep pushing—'tis wiser
  Than sitting aside,
And dreaming and sighing,
  And waiting the tide.
In life's earnest battle
  They only prevail
Who daily march onward
  And never say fail!

With an eye ever open,
  A tongue that's not dumb,
And a heart that will never
  To sorrow succumb—
You'll battle and conquer,
  Though thousands assail:
How strong and how mighty
  Who never say fail!

The spirit of angels
  Is active, I know,
As higher and higher
  In glory they go;
Methinks on bright pinions
  From Heaven they sail,
To cheer and encourage
  Who never say fail!

AUTHOR UNKNOWN

SHARING TOYS

If I had lots of building blocks
 And picture books and toys,
If I had trains and little cars
 Enough for twenty boys,
If I had drums and balls and kites,
 And ships like those at sea,
I still would want another child
 To come and play with me.

If I had games of every sort,
 A swing, and sand pile, too,
If I had tools for building things,
 And skates as good as new,
I would not want to play alone
 From dawn till set of sun;
For girls and boys are happiest
 When they can share their fun.

BLOSSOM BENNETT

LET OTHERS BE

When truth is at stake
 Defend it with might;
Stand firm as a rock,
 Upholding the right.
But in lesser things,
 That come up each day,
Learn not to insist
 On having your say.
Those who would live well
 Should early awaken,
And learn to let others
 Be mistaken.

ALICE CROWELL HOFFMAN

A LOFTY VISTA

These things shall be! A loftier race
 Then e'er the world hath known,
 shall rise
With flame of freedom in their souls
 And light of science in their eyes.

Nation with nation, land with land,
 Unarmed shall live as comrades
 free:
In every heart and brain shall throb
 The pulse of one fraternity.

New arts shall bloom of loftier mould,
 And mightier music thrill the
 skies;
And every life shall be a song,
 When all the earth is paradise.

JOHN ADDINGTON SYMONDS

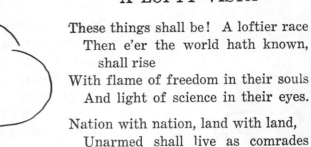

The Dreamer

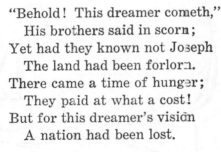

"Behold! This dreamer cometh,"
 His brothers said in scorn;
Yet had they known not Joseph
 The land had been forlorn.
There came a time of hunger;
 They paid at what a cost!
But for this dreamer's vision
 A nation had been lost.

The children tapped their foreheads,
 When he came by, and smiled.
He was an idle dreamer,
 They viewed him as a child.
Yet see! From out his dreamings,
 The Spanish flag unfurled,
And for his life's fruition
 Columbus found a world.

They called him visionary;
 The earth stood still, they said;
They made him make denial,
 This man with graying head.
The king heard not that whisper;
 "It moves," he muttered light;
To-day we give him honor—
 Galileo was right.

They called it "Fulton's Folly,"
 They said that it would fail;
The banks were lined with hundreds
 To jeer his work and rail.
Yet they were all dumbfounded;
 The crowd was put to shame;
And from this small beginning
 The ocean liner came.

They said that it was foolish
 To try the flight alone,
Across the trackless ocean
 Where none had ever flown.
But quietly and shrewdly,
 With scarce a backward glance,
He made his preparation—
 And Lindbergh flew to France!

Then scoff not at the dreamers,
 They pioneer the way;
They lead the ranks of progress,
 Are foremost in the fray.
Without these men of vision,
 Who scarce have thought of gain,
Our struggles all were useless,
 And sacrifices vain.

ARTHUR C. GWYNNE

THOUGHTS TO LIVE BY

THE BIBLE: PSALM 100

Make a joyful noise unto the Lord,
   all ye lands.
Serve the Lord with gladness.
Come before his presence with
   singing.
Know ye that the Lord he is God;
It is he that hath made us,
And not we ourselves.
We are his people,
And the sheep of his pasture.
Enter into his gates with thanks-
   giving,
And into his courts with praise,
Be thankful unto him,
And bless his name.
For the Lord is good;
His mercy is everlasting.
And his truth endureth to all
   generations.

A RULE FOR LIVING

Do all the good you can,
By all the means you can,
In all the ways you can,
In all the places you can,
At all the times you can,
To all the people you can,
As long as ever you can.

JOHN WESLEY

GROWTH

Fully, gladly, do the task
That each passing day may ask;

Do it with your strength and might,
Do it quickly, do it right;

Do it so when coming days
Bring fresh tasks in larger ways,

Strength of purpose, heart, and
   brawn
With greater skill will carry on.

M. LUCILLE FORD

FRONTIERS

Some people say there are no fron-
   tiers
Awaiting youth today;
That the chances our forefathers had
With time have passed away.
There are no new lands spread afar
Where the bold in heart may go.
That may be true, but think a while—
There are *new* frontiers, we know!

How many paths may still be left
In earth and air and sea,
Each with a call to the pioneer,
"Oh, come and follow me!"
Who knows the course or has a chart
Where the mind of man may seek
Some knowledge new, some wisdom
   true?
Of these frontiers I speak.

Oh, youth, the challenge is flung to
   you,
Your new frontiers to find.
There is no future bleak and bare
To an eager and earnest mind.
So bravely seek the hidden goals
And face each new frontier
With a conquering eye, with courage
   high,
And the heart of a pioneer!

M. LUCILLE FORD

AN HONEST ELF

I met a jolly elf one day,
   As jolly as could be;

And when I laughed at him
   He laughed right back to me;

But when I shouted angry words
   He growled ferociously.

His name was Echo and he knew
   Just what he was about;

As to his honesty there could
   Not be a bit of doubt,

For always he gave back to me
   The thing that I sent out.

He taught a lesson that will help.
   As through this life I go;

A lesson that will help me live
   And make my spirit grow—

That I'll get back just what I
   give
   To other folks, you know.

ALICE CROWELL HOFFMAN

INDEXES

Index of Titles with Authors

Index of Authors with Titles

Index of First Lines

115